Farm Fresh

Direct Marketing
Meats & Milk

Farm Fresh

Direct Marketing
Meats & Milk

by

Allan Nation

A division of Mississippi Valley Publishing, Corp.
Ridgeland, Mississippi

First Printing December 2002

© 2002 Allan Nation

Library of Congress Cataloging-in-Publication Data

Nation, Allan.
   Farm fresh : direct marketing, meats & milk / by Allan Nation.
      p. cm.
   Includes bibliographical references (p.).
   ISBN 0-9632460-9-7
     1. Meat--Marketing. 2. Milk--Marketing. 3. Dairy products--Marketing. 4. Direct selling. I. Title.

SF113.3 .N38 2002
664'.9'00688--dc21   2002029947

Cover Design by Steve Erickson, Ridgeland, MS

Manufactured in the United States of America

This book is printed on recycled paper.

Table of Contents

Anyone who is willing to use marketing as the basis for strategy is likely to acquire leadership in an industry or market fast and almost without risk.

Peter Drucker

Foreword

Congratulations! You have a product that you've decided to market directly to the consumer. Perhaps you've already figured out some of the advantages of direct marketing:

* By direct marketing you avoid the middle man who stands between you and the consumer.

* You have direct contact with your customers to learn first-hand their wants and needs–vital information for successful sales.

* By direct marketing you won't have to accept commodity prices over which you have no control. You can set your fees to reflect what your time and products are worth.

* You take home the full share of the marketing profits.

But there are other aspects of direct marketing you should consider:

* You, or someone in your family, must enjoy working with people, one-on-one, face-to-face.

* While all the profits come to you, so do all the expenses associated with marketing.

* Eliminating the middle man removes the buffer of shared risk if your venture fails or sales fall short of expectations.

* Are you able to juggle production to match your marketing, in order to avoid the risk of excess supply?

* The full burden of work–time and effort–falls to you.

7

In writing this book, we make the assumption that you have a quality product to sell. If you've chosen a product you truly love and can be proud to put your name on, your enthusiasm and passion can make up for the long hours and hard work necessary to turn your dream into reality.

Hopefully, this book will help you decide whether direct marketing is the correct route for the sale of your product. At the very least it will save you the heartache and expense of choosing the wrong marketing outlet for your farm or ranch. Working examples will offer further ideas to enhance your operation and cover aspects of direct marketing you may not have considered. A bibliography and resources offer further avenues for more in-depth research.

Ready? Read on.

Is Direct Marketing Right for You?

Anyone who thinks selling is easy has probably never done it. I first learned this when I was nine years old trying to sell pears from our family orchard on the side of the highway. I had a rolling fruit stand built on the frame of an old Model A pickup. I would make funny signs and stand beside the highway to try to flag people down. A lot of people would stop and listen to my earnest sales pitch. Most would just shake their heads and drive on. This rejection was tough to take at nine. It's just as tough today.

COMMODITY SALES PROS AND CONS

Most of us never consider that the lack of need for personal selling is the best thing about the commodity business. As long as you meet the specifications, you don't have to worry about creating a customer for your production. You can be a hopeless curmudgeon who hates people and bathes once a week and it won't make a dime's worth of difference in what you receive for your production.

> *The sole purpose of a business is to create a customer.*
> **Peter Drucker**

The commodity business allows you to grow as fast as your resources, capital and management skills allow. The market is so huge you could add a thousough head tomorrow and it wouldn't make a blip in the price. As a result, the commodity business most rewards those who have identified an unfair production advantage and who have geared themselves toward volume production.

Of course, all of us know the bad sides of commodity production, the worst part of which is an uncontrollable, ever-falling price for our production. The International Monetary Fund estimates that non-oil commodities are now one third their post-World War I price level. Since the turn of the century, commodities have declined in price on an average of 0.6% a year. This deflationary trend appears to be accelerating thanks to increased globalization of production.

A major weakness of commodity production is that it is an incomplete business whole. In fact, it is not

---

How Groceries Make Their Money

1. Low Transportation Costs. The customer pays his own transportation costs to and from the store.

2. Low Labor Costs. The customer uses his time and labor to assemble her own order and even sacks it herself in some stores.

3. Repeat Customers. This keeps advertising costs low.

4. No Receivables. The customer must pay at the time of purchase.

5. Long Payables. Most grocery stores do not pay suppliers for 90 days.

6. Low Cost of Goods. Grocery stores buy direct and in huge volumes to keep their cost of goods low.

really a business in the traditional definition. Business writer and management guru, Peter Drucker, said the sole purpose of a business is to create a customer. Customer loyalty provides the glue and stability that allows businesses to weather tough times and pass from one generation to the next. In commodities, prices matter more than personalities. The only thing the market cares about is can you meet the specs at the offered price?

DIRECT MARKETING, YOU CALL THE SHOTS

In contrast, with direct marketing you can call your price. While this solves one set of problems it produces others. With direct marketing you cannot produce one more pound of meat or milk than you can create a customer for. If you overproduce, you may not receive **any** price for the overproduction because it probably would not meet a commodity spec.

This makes direct marketing a higher risk than commodity production because production and marketing have to be kept in almost perfect balance. In fact, to achieve a premium price, demand must be kept slightly in excess of supply. This constant need to rein in the production horse is not natural for most farmers and ranchers.

In the commodity business, costs are determined by the price, this is termed a "price-based costing system." In this system, the price is always trying to stabilize at the breakeven

> *The person who owns the customer owns the deal.*

price of the average producer. As a result, only those with below average breakevens can even hope to make a consistent profit. Cost control is critically important in commodity production because costs are the only thing you can control.

In direct marketing, price is determined by your costs, or "cost-based pricing." This allows smaller, higher cost-per-unit producers to profit as well as lower cost, larger volume producers. Being small can actually be an advantage if you target a smaller market niche than the larger producer can cover with his much higher overheads.

> *A positioning statement says here is how I am different from the rest.*

Most successful businesses are expansions of the entrepreneur's own personal interests. It is very difficult to be successful as a marketer if you are not a member of the target audience. For example, a vegetarian will seldom be successful as a meat marketer.

The biggest way to overcome resistance is enthusiasm. If you aren't enthusiastic about what you are selling, I guarantee you won't be able to sell it.

WHOLESALE OR DIRECT?

The first rule of marketing is "the person who owns the customer owns the deal."

For example, Joel Salatin lives in the Shenandoah Valley of Virginia where he and his family raise pastured chickens, rabbits, grassfed beef lambs, and pigs at Polyface Farm. He has spent a number of years building a loyal customer base. Joel owns his customers. Therefore, he can dictate not only the price, but that his production will be seasonally available and customers will normally have to drive to the farm and get it. Joel could contract out the majority of his production to other farmers and it wouldn't mean a hoot to his customers as long as the quality were the same. However, if Joel were to sell through the local super-market, they would dictate the terms under which they would allow him access to their customers. This is the biggest difference between direct marketing and whole-saling and it is a **BIG** difference.

> # *What Kills New Businesses*
> *1. Running out of cash.*
> *2. Inability to raise money to fund expansion.*
> *3. Loss of control over expenses, inventories and receivables.*
> **Peter Drucker**

On a difficulty scale, consumer marketing through wholesale and retail is the most difficult and sophisticated marketing there is. In most instances, the supermarkets or health food stores will require a price low enough for a niche product in order to mark it up 30 to 50 percent without causing heart failure to their customers. This requirement largely eliminates the wide margin that makes artisanal production so attractive.

Supermarkets also want it available year-round and of consistent quality. This is very difficult to do with a fresh, grassfed product and the inherent wide production margin of direct grazing is lost for much of the year. Year-

> *Only two activities produce results. One is innovation. The other is marketing. Everything else just produces costs.*
> **Peter Drucker**

round consistent supply requires (at least some) irrigation, a lot of stored forage (grass and silages) or a huge amount of cooler space.

If you are going the wholesale route, you must be sure your production model can be ramped up as fast as sales increase or your efforts will just create a market for someone else to fill. Packaging becomes very important because it is virtually the only way to catch the fast-moving supermarket customer's eye.

Why Products Fail

Market researchers have found the five causes of wholesale distributed product failure are as follows:

1. A poorly articulated targeting and positioning strategy. 30 percent.

2. Product dissatisfaction. 30 percent.

3. Insufficient level of new product awareness. 20 percent.

4. Insufficient promotion. 10 percent.

5. Insufficient distribution. 10 percent.

It is interesting that product dissatisfaction caused only 30 percent of the failures. 70 percent were from poor marketing. The largest cause of marketing failure was from not narrowing your sales pitch enough.

A positioning statement says here is how I am different from all the rest. It cannot be longer than two sentences as that's as long as the average consumer will pay attention.

While you must differentiate yourself to justify your premium price, if you are selling through traditional supermarkets you must do this in such a way so as to not disparage the high-volume, commodity product. You may also have to pay a "stocking fee" to guarantee shelf space for your product. Also, you need to be aware that in some parts of the country the meat trade is heavily influenced by organized crime and can literally be a "cut-throat" business. Since supermarkets generally don't pay their bills for 90 days, it creates a cash flow problem for the producer.

ARE YOU WILLING TO SELL?

If you are considering getting into direct or wholesale marketing, I hope you are willing to sell. You don't have to like it. With few exceptions, financial success comes by doing what you dislike. True passions always evolve into chores. Everything is fascinating until you do it for a living. You will need to have multiple goals to avoid the "is that all there is?" feeling after accomplishing a long-sought goal.

You also need to be prepared for a drop in your interest and enthusiasm. I guarantee it will happen. Boredom is a sign that you have stopped learning and taking risks. Many entrepreneurs wreck their established businesses trying to regain the adrenaline high of their high-risk, startup days. If you choose direct marketing, I hope you like people and I hope you like yourself. I

> ## *Selling One, Two, Three*
> *First, learn how to do it, cook it for your family.*
> *Second, give some to your friends.*
> *Third, sell it to your friends' friends who ask for it.*

hope you have the personal self-confidence to be a little outrageous—a little bit of the showman. I hope your goal is to become a favorite guest on "Oprah."

I hope your idea of a fun evening is curling up with a good marketing book. I hope you will be willing to join your local Toastmaster's Club, become a member of the Chamber of Commerce and Sales and Marketing Executives Organization. There is a lot about marketing you can learn in your own community.

I also hope you've got a pretty thick hide. In niche marketing, 99 percent of the people you will approach are not your target customers. You can't let their rejection rattle you. Over time you will develop a pretty smart nose about who your customers are and where to find them.

Selling isn't ever easy, but it's about the best-paying job there is.

Marketing Meat Direct

Some of my personal observations on direct meat marketing are the following:

1. The marketing has to enhance grass production profits.

2. Try to avoid wholesaling through traditional retail outlets. The big mark up is from wholesale to retail.

3. Keep production costs low enough that your animals can still be sold through traditional markets at a profit.

4. *Sales should be seasonal and should concentrate on frozen meat. Older and heavier lambs and beeves are more profitable to produce and taste better than younger and lighter ones.*

5. *The leaner cuts of grassfed meats need special cooking instructions to prevent too high of a heat being used in cooking. Remember, low (heat) and slow is the way to cook lean grassfed meat.*

6. *Giving away or selling small samples of your meat is the best advertising. Consider a booth at the State or County Fair. These can both sell a lot of meat in a short amount of time and introduce new customers for your other sales.*

7. *Consider selling homemade sausage. This is an excellent way to sell mutton, the lower value cuts of beef and pasture produced pork.*

8. *Always be your own quality control. If it's not the best you've ever eaten, don't even think of selling it to others.*

While it may seem like there is a shortage of slaughter capacity in your particular area this usually isn't so. Even the biggest packers are willing to kill for you on a custom basis. What there is a shortage of is imagination and niche market development. Concentrate your efforts on marketing rather than on building a slaughter plant.

Questions to Answer Before you Begin Direct Marketing

* In the broadest terms, what is your area of expertise?

_____

_____

* In the narrowest terms, what unique niche do you fill that separates you from other grass farmers, in other words, your competition?

_____

_____

* Do you and/or members of your family enjoy meeting and working with the public?

_____

* Who among your family members has the most interest, enthusiasm and talent for direct marketing? If every family member will be involved discuss marketing options and delegate tasks and responsibilities.

_____

_____

_____

_____

_____

* Do you have room to expand—by adding products, installing freezer space to stretch your selling window beyond the seasonal availability of processed meats? How will this be accomplished and funded? Discuss goals, both short term and long term.

_____

_____

_____

_____

_____

* What is your core product? For example, if beef offers the most profit potential, is it necessary to offer fresh chickens and eggs as a lower-priced enticement to earn customers for the higher-priced beef?

_____

_____

* What will you do if demand exceeds the product? Can you fill orders with products from another farm–and guarantee the same quality that you produce?

_____

_____

* What is your marketing area–initially and after three to five years of growth?

Initially_____

_____

In 3 years_____

_____

In 5 years_____

_____

Long range _____

_____

_____

_____

_____

*Where will your business operation be located? Will your sales base be a fixed location, or cover varying locales? Are customers going to come to you, or will you go to your customers?

_____

_____

_____

* What area will be covered by your marketing?

Local?_____

Regional?_____

National?_____

* How will you reach your customers?

Advertising–how and where? _____

_____

Direct mail or e-mail? _____

How will you collect names for your database? Word of mouth?

_____

_____

Is a Web site necessary?_____

* How will you communicate with your customers?

Newsletter? Content? Frequency? _____

Walk-ins at business site? _____

Flyers? _____

Billboards? _____

Advertising? _____

Workshops or field days? _____

_____

_____

*What are you going to call your business?

_____

_____

* How will you price your product?

_____

_____

_____

_____

_____

* What spin offs can you add to "load up the wagon"? For example: workshops–how to cook meats French style, etc.? Hardware to go with the software? Jars of spice to complement the lamb? Field day open house? Selling other related products? Cheese or butter produced by a neighbor? Honey from the farm? Give away recipes?

_____

_____

_____

_____

_____

* How will you reward your best customers? Coupons for special discounts? Free dozen eggs?

_____

_____

* What will you do to encourage repeat business? Offer new products, new services, new locations? Give customers surveys to complete?

_____

_____

_____

_____

_____

_____

* How will you keep your business fresh and consumer friendly? Send out "valued customer" cards–at off-beat times: St. Patrick's Day to "remember the green in pasture-raised beef" or "It's barbecue season" for meat sales, for example.

_____

_____

_____

_____

* Who will investigate and handle legal matters: sales taxes, liability?

_____

* Who will share the work? Enlist family members. Set them up in self-contained enterprises or roles.

_____

_____

_____

_____

_____

* Analyze your lifestyle to be certain direct marketing works for you. For instance, if making farmstead cheese is your goal, will you be willing to handle processing, marketing, and other farm chores yourself? Are other family members willing to help? To what degree? Don't overlook time for routine chores–moving the herd, milking, cooking, cleaning, laundry, etc.

Guidelines for Surveys

Keep it simple.

Put a positive spin on questions. Don't ask for negatives–you'll get them whether you ask for them or not.

Avoid questions with yes or no answers.

Ask for suggestions for new services, locations, products.

Provide a self addressed envelope if immediate collection is not possible.

At Goose Pond Farm near Hartsell, Alabama, Charles and Laura Ritch's girls sing "Happy Trails to You" as they walk customers to their cars.

Success in direct marketing starts with the belief that how your food is produced matters.

Joel Salatin

All great results begin with naivety.

Tom Peters

First Things First — The Legalities

Historically, farmers have always sold their products directly to consumers. But in today's marketplace legal issues arise regarding customer satisfaction and liability, as well as safety concerns from processed foods. Special licenses or inspection procedures may be required for meat, milk or eggs. Much of these requirements vary from state to state.

Neil D. Hamilton, Director of the Agricultural Law Center at Drake University, has written *The Legal Guide for Direct Farm Marketing* (Drake University Agricultural Law Center, Des Moines, IA 50311) to answer just about every question you have, and many you may never even have thought about. If you're considering setting up an on-farm market or merely selling through your local Farmers' Market, this book covers land use and property law. Chapters address insurance and liability, advertising claims, employee issues, as well as certifica-

> *"By being a direct farm marketer, you become more than just a farmer, you may also become a retailer, an employer, a business manager, and even a food processor."*
>
> ***Neil D. Hamilton***

24

tions, licensing, labeling, taxation, inspections, exemptions and many other legal issues. The final chapter is devoted to marketing meat, poultry, eggs and dairy products.

Hamilton also notes that as you carry more products (processed items and non-food items), particularly those produced by other farmers, you become a "store" subject to an additional set of legal issues. Before beginning direct farm marketing, Hamilton lists six phone calls you should make:

1. To local land use planning authorities.

2. To your insurance agent.

3. To the state food inspection and licensing officials.

4. To the state labor commissioner.

5. To the state Department of Agriculture's

Follow the Rules

* *Processing meats—check with local, state, USDA regulations.*

* *Labeling—check with your state agriculture departments or extension services.*

* *Many livestock producers sell the animal "live" to the customer and add charges for slaughter and processing. State regulations vary as to the number of animals a farm can sell before USDA inspection is required. Check with your state's Department of Agriculture.*

In general smaller animals--chickens, pheasants, rabbits, fish—can be slaughtered on the farm. Larger livestock—goats, sheep, pigs, cattle—require state-inspected or a USDA approved plant.

marketing and diversification office.

    6. To your attorney.

    Whenever you have a question, the safest approach is to consult state or local officials.

    An appendix in Hamilton's book covers contacts for direct farm marketing resources in every state.

Finding Your Niche

The *Wall Street Journal* ran an article on the success Argentine grass-finished beef is having in upscale, trendy restaurants in the United States. While most people interviewed raved about the taste, one food critic in the article described the beef as "gamey" tasting. The *Journal* also noted that in Argentina there is a counter-movement among their upscale restaurants toward serving American-style grain-finished beef. The *Journal* was perplexed. Which beef was best?

Best for whom? When?

We don't all wear the same kinds of shoes, or drive the same car, why should we all have to eat the same kind of beef? Or at least the same kind of beef all the time? For an Argentinean, grain-finished beef is as exotic an experience as grass-finished is for an American. This is not so much a quality choice as just a choice.

In Switzerland, upscale restaurants offer diners a choice between American or Argentinean beef and both are priced equally premium to the local fare. That there can and should exist a market for more than one type of beef should not be so surprising.

For example, I like to eat at a Thai or Indian restaurant once or twice a year. However, I wouldn't want to eat Thai or Indian every day. Sometimes I don't want it better, I just want it different. Typically, the rarer and more exotic the food experience the more I am willing to pay to obtain it and pricey restaurants know this.

In another *Journal* article, they reported that upscale restaurants fly in exotic food items from all over the world by air freight to give their customers a rare, but pricey, eating experience. The point here is that there is far more money in making things "different" than in making things more alike. Not all of us want everything we eat to taste "just like chicken."

> *Jan and Will Holder of Eagle Creek, Arizona accidentally found niche markets for their grassfed beef. Or rather, niche markets found them.*
>
> *They first realized there was a niche market for premium priced organic beef pet food when a couple of groups of customers came to the ranch and asked for it. Similarly, a veterinary group that provides zoo diets appeared one day wanting to buy grassfed beef for their clients' lions and tigers. Apparently, grainfed beef makes lions and tigers sick.*
>
> *"The biggest lesson we have learned from this is that there is a market for anything," Will said.*

If the bison meat I order tastes just like beef, I'll be terribly disappointed. I order bison for it to be different, not necessarily better than a steak. I expect my venison to taste a little wild and exotic, and if it doesn't I'll stick with the steak. If the steak I order has no taste at all—and most calf-fed beef doesn't—I'll take veal, fish or chicken where I am expecting a flavor-less meat gussied up with a great tasting sauce.

The key point here is if I order something different I expect it to taste different. In a mostly bland-tasting world, any food with flavor, gamey or not, is a winner to me and apparently for a growing number of North Americans.

MAKE YOUR PRODUCT STAND OUT

Joel Salatin has frequently pointed out that the major marketing problem with grass-finished beef is that it is not dramatically different enough from store-bought commodity beef. He said that taste tests where most people cannot tell the difference between grass and grain finished beef are not good.

> *There is far more money in making things "different" than in making things more alike.*

In contrast, Joel's pasture-raised chicken and pork have a dramatically different taste and texture and would never be confused with the store-bought brand. As a result, these products can demand a higher price and yet still be much easier to sell.

I visited with the manager of a large Western cow-calf-yearling ranch who was wanting to start a grass-finished beef program with a startup size of 50,000 head a year. I told him if it was me I would concentrate on heiferettes (young cows) and let the steers keep going to the feedlots as heavy feeders. There are a couple of reasons for this. One, in his seasonal environment he would not be able to "finish" but one set of cattle a year. This is not a problem

> *Niche marketing requires that you concentrate on a small group of people and ignore everyone else.*

for graziers selling 20 freezer beeves but would be a major problem on the scale he was contemplating.

29

Two, even a 1000-lb steer will bring more as a feeder than a finished steer seven years out of ten. The whole reason for going to the trouble of creating something different is to get a higher price.

You should attack on as narrow a front as possible. You cannot defend success gained on a broad front.

Peter Drucker

New things must have a period of "windfall profits" to reward the entrepreneur for the trouble. In contrast to the steer, a heiferette is a price-discounted class of animal at auction all year long. She can be finished (fattened) on grass easily and fast, and is young enough to still have tender beef with a strong beef flavor.

In France, where eating is a major entertainment, the heiferette is the premium-priced class of animal due to its flavor. There is no mistaking this beef for veal. This beef has a taste! It may be too strong for some, but for people who are seeking a different taste it will not disappoint.

To make the experience even more exotic, I suggested he market it as "Full-Flavored, French-style Gourmet Beef" and cater exclusively to upscale restaurants in San Francisco. Remember, there are no Kansas City steaks in Kansas City. Things always taste better (different) if they come from "away."

The more different your product is from the mainstream, the more consumer and media attention it will attract.

I have a feeling American-produced grass-finished beef will sell better touted as Argentine-style beef than as range-fed as some are marketing it. One sounds sexy and exotic and the other sounds local and backyard.

IT'S ALL ABOUT PERCEPTION

A major problem with non-organic grassfed beef is that it isn't **perceived** to be different enough from ordinary beef to make an emotional difference to most consumers. The key word here is emotional.

Currently, getting a premium for grassfed beef requires the customer to "buy into" the whole idea of open space, green grass, blue skies and health values. This requires a pretty time-consuming marketing presentation.

While this may fit well in a garden club or civic group presentation, it doesn't fit well in a supermarket setting. It's very difficult for a new product to attract attention just by sitting on the shelf. Most people shop as fast as they can and will not "see" a new product unless they are looking for it.

WHY WEIRD WORKS

The biggest word in marketing is new. Almost all food categories in the United States and Canada are fully mature. This means they cannot naturally grow any faster than the population increases. To grow in such an environment requires you to wrest market share away from

> *If a new venture is not totally market-focused, if not market driven, then it will succeed only in creating an opportunity for a competitor.*
>
> **Peter Drucker**

established brands. For a minimally capitalized, start-up brand, this is next to impossible. This is one reason why being weird works.

Unless the product category is very new or changing quickly (or both) the likelihood of attracting new users is very slim. Consequently, startup food products are only likely to find success in very new or rapidly changing categories.

Rapid growth is why the venture capital community and Wall Street is so attracted to organic production. Currently, it is the only rapidly growing food category. Investors know those who can get in early and establish a brand name can occupy the high ground and play defense against the late-comers.

> *In the commodity world "being different" always brings a discount. In the direct marketing world "being different" can result in a premium.*

Consequently, in the establishment phase of a new market it is not necessary to be profitable to attract Wall Street's attention, it is just necessary to "be there" and have an exciting growth story about the future. For example, Horizon Organic Dairy in Colorado raised $50 million on Wall Street despite losing a million dollars a year running a large scale organic feedlot dairy (which they subsequently sold).

The more different your product is from the mainstream, the more consumer and media attention it will attract. Public relations should always come first. However, public relations can seldom do it all. Advertising is controllable and targetable and it works for you even when you are off on vacation in Peru. Interestingly, another benefit of an unusual production model is that it will attract **few**

> *If your neighbor thinks your idea for a new business is a good one, it probably isn't different enough to make any money.*
>
> **Peter Drucker**

competitors irrespective of your personal success. The average farmer or rancher is fascinated by new ideas, but only as an entertainment. He doesn't want to do them himself.

For example, Joel Salatin makes about as much noise about being able to make $100,000 a year from 100 acres of grass as one human being is capable of, and yet not a single farmer in his community has seriously tried to replicate what he is doing. That consumers are attracted and competitors are repelled by the radically new is a win-win situation for the entrepreneur as it gives you an extended period of wide production margins.

POSITIONING

A key element in marketing is positioning. People like a mental peg to hang a product on. An undifferentiated product only brings the commodity (market-clearing) price. Heaven help you if you have an undifferentiated "different" product.

In the commodity world "being different" always brings a discount, whereas, in the marketing world "being different" can result in a premium— often a big premium. The really big money in ranching has always

> *Big companies need big volumes to cover big overheads.*

been in seeking out discounted animals and "upgrading" them with marketing. Buying at a discount and selling at a premium produces the large margin a startup operation must have to survive on its initial low volume.

For example, Holstein steers sell at a discount to traditional beef breeds. In every taste test I have ever seen, the Holsteins usually win, so it is not because the beef tastes bad. It is because the cuts look different in the meat case. Consequently, they are harder to sell.

However, Holstein cuts do not look different to Polish or Russian people. They look like home. In cities like Chicago and New York where there are large numbers of recent immigrants from Eastern Europe, somebody could develop a sizable niche market for grass-finished Holsteins by calling it "Polish-style" or "Russian-style" or "Continental-style" beef.

> *Niche market development is almost always a job left to the entrepreneur.*

White tuna was a difficult sell until a smart marketing guy added "Guaranteed not to turn pink in the can." Now white tuna is the dominant brand. I think a smart marketer could make yellow-fat beef a premium-priced product.

The big question is whose job is it to do this marketing?

A packer was on one of our conference programs 15 years ago. He said he thought it was wrong that grass-finished beef brought a discount because he personally thought it ate just as good as grain-finished. A woman in the audience asked why he didn't get his company to advertise that fact.

With a world-weary look and a groan he answered, "Look lady, I'm not in the education business. I'm in the killing business."

> *Do not be afraid of growing slowly. Be afraid of standing still.*
> **Chinese proverb**

Commodity-based packers have built their "unfair advantage" on production volume or what they call "through-put." They are not interested in creating differentiated products because that would slow the through-put and make raw material (live cattle) acquisition much more difficult and costly.

This holds true in all industries. Big companies need big volumes to cover big overheads. Long production runs produce low costs. Consequently, niche market development is almost always a job left to the entrepreneur.

A GAME PLAN FOR NICHE MARKETERS

A niche market has been described as a "hole in the marketplace."

The reason niche markets are so sought after is that they provide the highest margins per unit of production. These wide margins allow minimally financed companies to start small and fund their growth from their customers rather than outside investors. These high margins exist because the first occupier of a niche has no competition. You have, in

> *A niche marketer is a pioneer.*

effect, a monopoly position. And, monopolies are where the big margins are.

Too many graziers thinking about direct marketing are sitting back hoping someone else will pioneer a market in their area and thereby prove its existence. This is akin to a general allowing the enemy to occupy a hill and dig in before attacking it. It is almost a recipe for suicide.

Just as in war, in marketing getting there first with the most is an incredible tactical advantage that is very difficult to overcome. It is estimated that the second comer to a niche has to have a value proposition ten times better than the first to even attract attention.

What a niche marketer is looking for is an undefended hill to capture. Even an unarmed two-year-old can capture an unoccupied hill.

35

This absolute need to be out there all by yourself doesn't feel right to most commodity producers. Here's why.

In the commodity business there are definite cost advantages to locating in production "clusters" where everyone is concentrating on a similar commodity. These clusters have cheaper production inputs and services because the market is large enough to produce competition and input suppliers and services. Marketing is even enhanced because in most commodities the product will have to be shipped out of the production area to be sold. The more of it there is the lower the transportation cost. For example, the cost per ton hauled by a unit train is a fraction of that hauled by a truck.

> *Wide margins are only found in small markets.*

And again, a larger market attracts more buyers, which results in a better price for everyone. As a result, being "different" in the commodity world seldom pays as well as "fitting in." No doubt, this dichotomy between what is good for business in commodities and what is good in direct marketing is what is so confusing about direct marketing.

> *The marketer defines a niche.*

A niche marketer is a pioneer. He wants to be out there all by himself. When the neighborhood starts getting crowded he will pick up stakes and move into a new wilderness where he can be by himself again. This need for loneliness makes sense in direct marketing as high margins can only exist as long as there is no competition.

You must have a monopoly.

So, who defines a niche? The marketer does.

NOISY AND DIFFERENT

Every piece of communication a niche marketer produces must scream, "I am different" and then define that difference to your potential customers. This "difference" defines and circumscribes the niche that you plan to serve.

This need to be noisy and different goes against the grain of most farmers and ranchers who want to be peers and colleagues with their neighbors.

A niche marketer doesn't want a neighbor within 500 miles doing what he is doing. This is why highly unusual production models are better than conventional ones. As Joel Salatin has pointed out, you want to be seen as a "lunatic farmer" because that keeps away competition.

This is why a mini-cheese plant on the Alabama Gulf Coast is far more likely to find a far more lasting and profitable market niche than one in Wisconsin. No one in your area raising lambs or pastured poultry? Wonderful!

Niche Marketing Strategy

1. Look for a market with no competition.
2. Be as different as possible and communicate that difference.
3. Concentrate on profits rather than gross sales.
4. Use early wide margins to build a defensive position that will allow you to lower your prices to stave off later small-scale competition.
5. Sell at the first sign of public company competition.

If a dozen people are doing it, forget it. The high ground has already been taken. Remember, in a niche market you are looking for what doesn't exist. Not what does. Peter Drucker said a good judge of the validity of a niche market is to ask your neighbor what he thinks of it. If he agrees it is a good idea, it is probably not different enough to succeed as a niche market.

The beauty of being first is that normally you will have five to eight years of high margin monopoly before the interlopers are convinced your market is for real.

He said the response you are seeking is guarded skepticism not enthusiasm. With a niche-oriented business it is far riskier to hew too closely to the commonplace than it is to get too far out. What absolutely will not work is a smaller version of a successful large business.

Large businesses use volume to overcome small margins per unit of production. Take the volume away and they cannot be profitable. Small businesses have to have wider margins to be viable. Wide margins are only found in small markets.

My Dad always said the beauty of the United States was that its domestic market was so large that just about any peculiar interest you have could be turned into a profitable business. The operative word here is peculiar.

Again, people who need wide-scale acceptance are unlikely to be successful niche marketers. The vast majority of people are not going to want what you are selling and many may even be hostile to you. The widest margins are found in markets that target no more than two percent of the population. Can you stand being rejected by 98 percent of the people you try to sell to?

SUCCESS IS THE KILLER

Interestingly, it is not choosing a niche market too small that undoes most niche players. What kills niche marketers is success.

If you grow your niche market to around $15 million a year in sales, you will attract public company attention. Probably the wisest thing to do at that point is to sell. In fact, this could be your planned exit strategy. The unfair advantage public companies have is a very low cost of money. If you get into a fair fight with

> *Price can't stop passion.*

them on a dollar for dollar basis, a small private company is sure to lose.

In markets with less than $15 million, your primary competitors will be people pretty much like yourself. They are attracted to your market by the wide margins you are enjoying and would like some for themselves.

Therefore, the best defense against these bootstrapping interlopers is to lower your prices. This denies them the margins they need to self-finance growth and effectively prevents them from ever growing into a serious competitor.

> *Command of the stage comes from one thing: pleasure. And you can't communicate pleasure unless you feel it.*
>
> **Phillippe Gaulier**

The beauty of being first is that normally you will have five to eight years of a high margin monopoly before the interlopers are convinced that your market is for real. You need to be using those years to dig your trenches and lay your land mines in order to prepare for the inevitable attack from your competition.

THE NICHE WITHIN THE NICHE

As niche markets grow and become successful they become susceptible to being "sub-niched."

A phenomenon noted during the high tech boom of the 1990s was that every successful niche tended to create at least two successful sub-niches. Apparently no one can create a tent large enough to satisfy everyone. The more watered-down and compromised a niche becomes in order to attract mainstream customers and grow the more susceptible it becomes to being sub-niched.

> *Every successful niche tends to create at least two successful sub-niches.*

A good example of sub-niches can be found in the history of Christianity. Originally Christianity was a tiny niche market and there was but one Christian church. However, as Christianity became bigger and more successful the church began to splinter into multiple sub-niches of belief that emphasized often minute points of disagreement.

Looking at modern-day Christianity, as the large denominations tried to appeal to the mainstream public with an increase in secularism, they drove their most fervent believers to new niche churches that offered the promise of an unquestioning, faith-based "old-time religion."

> *It is better to lose sales to yourself than to someone else.*

Another example of this sub-niching can be found in the USA's organic food industry today. As organic food has found acceptance and become the darling of the supermarket it has increasingly come to resemble mainstream agriculture. For example, most large-scale organic farms use the same industrialized production model as conventional farms. Others have become divisions of publicly held companies.

Now, there is a sub-niche forming that is saying that the production model used is just as, or more, important as the inputs used. This group of people is rallying to a still ill-defined standard they call "beyond organic" which celebrates small-scale, "natural" production models.

> *Looking at nature, we see that nothing that grows starts large; it always starts small. No one is "in charge" of making growth occur. We need more gardeners and fewer CEOs.*
>
> **Peter Senge**

Many of the customers of this new sub-niche are the old customers of the original organic niche but who are now turned off by the large-scale corporate farming of modern organic agriculture.

Equally dismayed are many of today's successful large organic producers who now find themselves the "establishment" and under attack by people who philosophically highly resemble themselves from 20 years ago. Unfortunately, there has been no successful defense found against a sub-nicher who has indeed found a group of disgruntled customers. The defense I described earlier of lowering your prices doesn't work against a sub-nicher because he has found a hole in your defenses and is going after passionate people who believe the way he does. Price can't stop passion. True believers don't care what it costs.

THE ONLY DEFENSE IS OFFENSE

The only defense against being sub-niched is to sub-niche yourself.

You need to keep an ear to the ground and listen for rumblings within your consumer base. Once you identify the source of their dissatisfaction see if you can't come up with a different product that satisfies their needs.

Will a new product cannibalize your existing product?

Maybe. However, Sergio Zyman the former marketing director for Coca-Cola said that if your old products can't withstand the competition it is only a matter of time before your competitors figure that out as well.

He said it is better to lose sales to yourself than to someone else. Ideally, this sub-niche product line should not even appear to be from your company.

For example, if Horizon Organic Milk decided to come up with a totally grassfed, certified CLA milk to satisfy that market niche it should not be identified with Horizon Milk.

Become A Legend in Your Own Time

The alternative spelling of legend is "guts." Legends are people who act so daringly that they become larger than life. Do the unusual, the unexpected and you give yourself a wider platform on which to operate. Others expect you to be comfortable with risk, and they trust you with risk. Start to build your own legend and you stop worrying about criticism. You begin to do something that fits in no known category.

Harriet Rubin

Much of the resentment of Horizon is that they are a large publicly owned company that is perceived to have run rough shod over smaller organic dairy producers. Why drag that baggage along with your new product?

People seeking an alternative to Horizon don't want it to be called Horizon. Any product

> ### *Peter Drucker's Rule:*
> *Lakecomers to the new must be ten times better than what they hope to displace.*

that is directed to a different group of consumers should always have its own separate identity. Otherwise it is very confusing to the consumer. To a consumer a product cannot be but one thing.

Remember, a niche market is a hole in the marketplace. It is also a hole in a person's mind. Once that hole is filled with a product's name it is almost impossible to replace it.

This is why whether you are playing niche or sub-niche marketing being first to market and more importantly first into the consumer's mind is 99% of the marketing game.

NEW NICHES DISCOVERED EVERY DAY

One day an elegantly dressed African-American with a British accent arrived at Joel Salatin's farm in rural Virginia. The man inquired if Joel might have some elderly chickens for sale.

Joel replied that he had some frozen spent laying hens he could sell.

The man said that would be fine and took all that Joel had in his freezer.

Joel said he was really happy because spent hens had always been difficult to sell.

The next day the man returned and asked if Joel

43

had any more spent hens for sale.

"How many more?" Joel asked.

"Approximately 600 a week should do for a start," the man replied.

Joel said that he must have looked somewhat shocked until the man explained that he was with an Embassy of a large African country in Washington, D.C. His staff was growing increasingly restless and had been threatening to return to Africa.

"None of them can stand the taste of American chicken," he explained.

"But they love the taste of your fine hens. You have saved our day."

Joel said that once you think you've got all of your niches covered a new one will appear.

Preparing a Business and Marketing Plan

A business plan is a sales tool. It is primarily written to sell one of three audiences: An investor, a banker, or yourself.

Each of these audiences requires a different business plan because each perceives the risk involved differently. If you go broke, both the banker and the investor lose their money. But, if you succeed the investor gets filthy rich and the banker gets his money back with a little interest.

Business plans for investors need to be in the context of big ideas that could change the world. Business plans for bankers need to stress the lack of risk to them. Business plans for yourself need to convince you

> *Business plans must be different, and they should have multiple purposes.*

this is something you absolutely must do for your long-term personal happiness and sanity.

The best recommendation for an investor or banker is a previous business success.

The more like the business you are contemplating is to what you have already done the more credible your business plan will be.

A plan should have multiple purposes: To get

help from others. To use as a guide for running operations once the business is underway. And to force entrepreneurs to appreciate the difficulty of the task they face.

The first question you must answer is: "What distinctive competence does my business have that will set it apart from others?" You absolutely must have an unfair advantage to be successful in a new business.

> *Give yourself permission to dream big dreams.*

The operational plan determines how much you will sell, to whom and at what price. No business plan is really credible until you create your first customer.

Will you quit under pressure? The biggest risk to both the investor and the banker is that you will quit under stress. Both need to be convinced that you will go the full course, no matter what.

THE INVESTOR BUSINESS PLAN

Your numbers must be very impressive. Your revenue forecast in the fifth year has to be about 25 times the investment you are looking for to interest most investors. The starting point for valuing private businesses is ten times annual earnings. For publicly traded companies this can be twice this figure or more. Your Business Plan must convince an investor that:

1. A market exists.
2. Your product will satisfy the market need.
3. Your marketing plan has a high probability of connecting the two.

How are you going to sell them?

The Marketing Plan should identify how your business will identify, contact and sell to its customers. A marketing plan with no paid advertising will be considered naive.

A business that has not developed a prototype product is generally considered too risky for an investment. The most credible way to prove your business plan is to start a business on a very small scale.

Only really new ideas can attract investors. Investors are looking for rapid and sustained growth. This means an annual rate of 40 to 50 percent compounded for five to six years. Such high growth rates only happen in NEW industries. In a mature industry, every dollar of sales must be taken away from someone else. That doesn't happen fast.

Don't hold back. A business plan for an investor should try to envision a really big dream. Most people limit the amount of success they can have in life by not allowing themselves to day dream. Give yourself permission to make your day dreams ten times larger than you have in the past. Venture capitalists are more afraid of people who dream too small than those who dream too big.

> ## Investors look at:
> 1. *What the business is.*
> 2. *The MONEY.*
> 3. *Who's behind it.*

Investors expect an entrepreneur to personally subsist on as little as possible while the business is getting off the ground. Don't put yourself in for a big salary on their money.

Investors prefer hired management who can be fired to equity partners who can't. The entrepreneur's initial stake is often intentionally diluted by the investor by the promotion of fast-growth strategies that create negative cash flows. Since the entrepreneur cannot match the investor's ability to put additional monies in the business, his stock percentage is greatly reduced or even eliminated.

A BUSINESS PLAN FOR A BANKER

Bankers can be better partners than investors because they are not interested in gaining control of your business or in replacing you (in most cases). Unlike investors, bankers are very wary of business plans showing rapid growth. They know that cash flow is a major problem for rapid growth companies and you may not be able to repay your loan.

> *You can achieve any great vision of yourself if your work gives you pleasure.*
>
> **Jacques Lecoq**

Both bankers and investors are wary of people with advanced degrees. They prefer people with moderate but not extensive educations. The older and more experienced you are the less important is your formal education.

Bankers don't like startups. You can seldom borrow money for a startup enterprise. Unlike the investor, the banker requires that the market already be established. Bankers love history and security.

What do you personally bring to the table? A banker's first question is usually, "What makes you think you can run this business profitably?"

Act like you don't need the money.

To borrow money you must create the attitude that while you would like to have the loan, you don't really need it. Bankers like to lend to successful people

---

Bankers will lend to startups only if:

1. The business and the person look good.

2. The loan is fully collateralized.

3. The company shows substantial equity.

> # *Bankers are primarily interested in:*
> *1. The existence and stability of cash flows to service the debt.*
> *2. A proven market with a plan for reaching it.*
> *3. The competence and experience of management.*

seeking to create bigger and better things.

Loving what you do is important.

Bankers love it when your primary drive comes from a love of what you are doing.

Bankers love cash flow.

Who are you?

Bankers like to lend money to people they know personally and who are well-known in their community.

Bankers like to lend short-term. Bankers see short-term loans as less risky than long-term.

Bankers like real estate lending. They are more comfortable with financing land and equipment than operations. They hate inventory that fluctuates in value.

Use the banker where he is most comfortable. Because with land and equipment, what you are buying stands for most of the collateral. You should not put your own capital into these items. Use your capital for marketing and operations.

Bankers hate fixed costs.

Bankers like businesses that can generate cash flows without high fixed cost investments.

The interest on a bank loan has to be paid whether the business is making money or not. When a loan goes into default all principle and interest is due immediately. This is usually a prelude to bankruptcy.

A Banker's Checklist

1. Description of the nature and operation of the business and brief summary of its history.
2. General plan for the future operation of the business including how the proposed loan will help the business reach its goals.
3. The exact amount and purpose of the loan.
4. Proposed repayment terms.
5. Capital structure of the business. What is the debt/equity ratio. How much of your money is invested versus the banks'.
6. Details of any leasing agreements you have entered.
7. The collateral being proposed for the loan.
8. Amount of insurance carried on the business.
9. Breakdown of assets owned.
10. Current and prior years financial statements.
11. Federal tax returns for the last three years.
12. Proposed financial statements for the next three years.
13. Summary of the assumptions which underpin your financial projections.
14. A worst case scenario.
15. Your professional qualifications including your work history and education.
16. Your credit history and references.
17. A personal financial statement.
18. Copies of your personal income tax returns for the last three years.

A BUSINESS PLAN FOR YOURSELF

A job is not a business. Creating a job for yourself is not a business. In a business, other people provide the labor for your dreams.

While self-employment may be a necessary means to an end, it should never be the final result of a business plan.

Is the jump worth the candle?

The primary purpose of a personal business plan is to determine if the end result justifies the aggravation and sacrifice required to obtain it.

> ## *The 5 Steps for Food*
> *1. Learn how to produce it.*
> *2. Produce it for yourself and your family.*
> *3. Give some to your friends.*
> *4. Sell it to your friends' friends who ask for it.*
> *5. Make it a business.*

A new business must be smarter.

A new business must be smarter (in the areas where it chooses to compete) than the old business it seeks to supplant.

Do your homework first.

Success starts with personal belief.

Successful direct marketing starts with the personal belief that how your food is produced matters.

> ## *3 Workable Strategies*
> *1. Least cost producer.*
> *2. Differentiation— unique features that add value (guaranteed CLA, etc.).*
> *3. Niche market (organic, etc.)*

If you don't personally see a necessity for a particular production peculiarity, you won't be able to convince your customer of its importance either.

Different gets more attention. Keep in mind that the more different you can make your product from the commonplace, the easier it will be to get attention for it.

LEARN YOUR TRADE FIRST

The most expensive education you will ever buy is trying to teach your customer and learn your trade at the same time.

Peter Drucker said a good rule of thumb to judge a new business idea is "Will the annual net income after 12 years equal the initial equity investment required?" Are you willing to put the years in? Where are you in your own lifecycle? Are you willing to put in the twelve years a new business requires to become profitable?

> *The unique attributes of a food product won't matter if it doesn't taste good.*

Most new businesses will require:

1. Two years of intense study of the market and identification of the critical factors required for success before starting the business.
2. Three to five years to break even on cash flow.
3. Twelve years to show a positive return on the initial investment.

Self-finance is necessary for a prototype. Most new businesses are initially financed by the entrepreneur himself and/or his immediate family and friends. Business is a game of swapping margin for volume. It is extremely difficult to have both high margins and high volume.

Why will customers leave your competition? To be believable your plan must convincingly describe why customers will forsake the competition. You must be certain that the values you are selling are the values cherished by the customer.

Why new businesses lose money: It costs as much or more to create a new customer as you receive for the product. There is no profit until the customer repurchases your product. Old customers are very profitable because they have no marketing costs. All very profitable businesses are created by old customers.

> # *Niche Businesses*
> *1. High returns on low volumes require that there be no competition.*
> *2. Why will this niche continue?*
> *3. Why won't larger firms move in?*

Why marketing can never stop: The best businesses will lose 20 to 25 percent of their customers a year. A 20 percent decrease in old sales will require 25 percent more new sales just to stay even. It can take many years to recover from one year's cessation in marketing to new customers.

Success kills niches. The primary limitation to niche marketing strategy is that one can't be too successful.

> # *Your market must be described in terms of*
> *1. Size*
> *2. History*
> *3. Recent growth trends*
> *4. Expected future growth*
> *5. Geography*

Everything eventually becomes a commodity.

Anything that can be produced easily on a small scale can be produced on a large scale cheaper.

Given time all easy-to-produce products become commodities.

Skill requirements produce lasting niches.

Your long-lasting niches are those that require a great deal of personal skill to master.

> ### Risk Assessment
>
> *(1 is least risky. 4 is highest risk.)*
> 1. *Old products/old customers*
> 2. *New products/old customers*
> 3. *New customers/old products*
> 4. *New products/new customers*

Low skill niches seldom last over five to eight years. Any product differentiation has to be credible and demonstrable. For example, you must use credible scientific references for all health claims.

Being square pays.

Most customers will allow you only one unconventionality. If you are selling an unconventional product, everything else about you needs to be very conventional for you to retain your credibility.

> ### Some long term niche marketing strategies to consider are:
> 1. *To have a planned sale in five years.*
> 2. *To move into a more differentiated product.*
> 3. *To reinvest profits to increase scale and thereby lower costs.*

Personal Assessment

1. Are you a self-starter?
2. Do you like and get along with people?
3. Are you older than 30 years of age?
4. Did you have a small business as a child?
5. Do you spend a lot of time day dreaming?
6. Have you ever been fired?
7. Is to be your own boss your main reason for starting a business?
8. If you failed and lost all of your family's savings could you accept it as a learning experience, and be willing to try again?
9. Do you like games where you can improve your chances of winning through learning?
10. Have you ever managed other people?
11. Do you become totally involved in your work? Do you talk about it incessantly?
12. Are you prepared to work 80 hour weeks for an indefinite number of years?
13. When you play sports is winning very important to you?
14. Do you actively join church, civic and other groups?
15. Do you seek out experts before tackling new projects?
16. Can you do several things at the same time?
17. Are you a well organized person?
18. Are you personally healthy?
19. Are you financially healthy?
20. Can you handle conflict with other people?
21. Can you make decisions quickly?
22. Do you find learning new things to be great fun?
23. Do you read marketing and business management books in your spare time?
24. Do you avoid negative people like the plague?
25. Do you read the *Stockman Grass Farmer* cover to cover each month?

Skills Assessment

What skills do I have?
What skills do I need?
Can I hire it done or do I need to know it personally?
(If you can hire it done, you should.)
Concentrate your efforts on skills that are rare.
Assess the strengths of each contributing person.
Turn goals into a realistic flow chart.
Set up a checks and balance system to make sure the work gets done.

Value Assessment

Do your customers look like you?
Do you look like your customers?
What is the value network of your customer?
Does your product capture your customers' values?
Does your chosen product differentiation really matter to your customer?
Does your family see your business goals as particularly worthy and important?
Are they willing to lower their current lifestyle for several years to see you achieve them?
Are you willing to accept a divorce to achieve your business goals?

MARKETING 101

The easiest people for you to sell to are those who share the same values you do. However, to increase volume you may have to sell to people who do not share your values. Never try to change a person's pre-existing values. Come up with different products that reflect their values instead.

Do not try to expand the market of a pre-existing product by diluting its current market positioning. This could cause you to lose your current customers faster than you gain new ones. Remember, no one wants a product designed for everyone.

The size of the niche you target and the price you charge are very closely interrelated. The smaller the niche you serve, the higher the price you can charge. Your customer should not expect you to live in poverty in order to serve his narrowest needs. If he does, don't target him as a customer. Here are some things to think about for your marketing plans:

Jan Moseley, a bison grazier near Dallas, Texas, said that once she saw meat marketing in a game context it became fun. Now, she finds it exhilarating. "I call it the art of shameless self-promotion," she said. While most of her grassfed bison meat is sold wholesale to retailers, she makes more on direct sales.

To encourage direct sales she printed a brochure inviting people to visit the ranch and "experience bison." These are placed in area campgrounds and motels. Some 100 people showed up one June for "Baby Bison Day" to see the new calf crop.

She also publishes a quarterly newsletter for direct customers called "Bison Bits." A copy is sent to all area schools to encourage student tours of the ranch.

Work with nice people. Joel Salatin requires all of his customers to be nice people. Anyone who is cranky and abusive gets "tossed out of the box" and is never notified of another sales period. I think this is a great idea and everyone should do this.

Seek educated customers. Marketing studies have found that education level is far more important than income in niche-food marketing. Generally, the higher the education level you target, the more responsive the consumer is to health-related marketing pitches and the less sensitive they are to the price. For example, school teachers are not highly paid but

> *Tauna Powell of Meadville, Missouri said her doctor became a customer for her grassfed meat after reviewing her blood work during a checkup. "If eating grassfed beef has done that for you, I've got to have some," he said.*

are excellent potential customers. (Local schoolteachers are the core of Joel Salatin's customers.) In college and university towns, the faculty (not the students) make excellent marketing targets. Cities like Seattle and Austin, where large numbers of people make their living in intellectual, high-tech pursuits are excellent markets. In contrast, blue-collar traditional towns are much tougher.

Welcome newcomers. Newcomers to a community make good prospects because they have left all their traditional suppliers behind and are open to new products and suppliers. This is why fast-growing towns are better markets for new-idea food products than slow-growing, stagnant towns.

Target women. The most responsive customer

for premium priced health-related foods is a middle to upper middle class, well-educated woman.

Go after health sensitive consumers. What will change eating habits in people of all ages is a major health crisis. Therefore, cancer and heart attack support and survivor groups are excellent potential markets for health-related food products.

Doctors who follow naturopathic medicine can be good allies for grassfed meat and dairy products. Nutritional guidance is frequently a part of the patient's overall health program.

Naturopathic medicine emphasizes the use of diet, exercise, nutritional supplements, herbal remedies, homeopathy, detoxification, counseling, physical medicine, and more traditional approaches such as "nature cures" and hydrotherapy.

Naturopathic medical colleges emphasize the need to study health as well as disease. The prevention of disease and the attainment of optimal health in patients are primary objectives. In practice, these objectives are accomplished

David Vetter of Marquette, Nebraska believes that grassfed beef and grain production are very compatible.

His farm The Grain Place grows organic corn, sorghum, popcorn, and soybeans in a long rotation with permanent pasture upon which he grows grassfed beef. The farm's grain is processed on the farm and sold to small specialty organic food manufacturers all over the country. The grassfed beef is sold locally. With a major Interstate highway a few miles away, he hopes to make the organic farm a major tourist stop.

Vetter said he got the marketing bug early in life and loves to sell. "Marketing is the most profitable input in farming because it is a pure return to knowledge," he said.

through education and the promotion of healthy ways of living.

Others in the medical field. Holistic doctors, chiropractors, dentists, osteopaths and homeopaths all frequently use diet recommendations in the treatment and prevention of disease. Many of these are predisposed toward recommending local suppliers of grassfed meat and dairy products. Let them know you exist.

Some Sources of an Unfair Advantage

A STRENGTH is something your business does exceptionally well.

A DISTINCTIVE COMPETENCE is something you do well compared to the competition.

A COMPETITIVE ADVANTAGE is an edge over others in the same market.

WHY YOU MUST KEEP MARKETING

The biggest mistake most new businesses make is misjudging how many of this year's customers will be there next year. Once production and marketing are in balance most people tend to slack off or even stop looking for new customers. This is a big mistake. Here's why:

Most businesses run on a retention rate of between 50 and 80 percent. If you are at the high end of the range (80 percent) and you have 100 customers this year, you will have to find 20 new customers just to stay at the same level of business next year.

This customer attrition factor is why marketing can never stop and must be continuous.

What to Name It

The most important marketing decision you will ever make is what to name your product. The best name to use is your own. Frank Perdue's Chicken. Laura's Lean Beef. Coleman's Beef. Bryan Hotdogs. Colonel Sanders' Fried Chicken. McDonald's Hamburgers. Jimmy Dean's Sausage.

Unless you are selling an ethnic product, an Anglo-Saxon sounding surname has been found to be the best for marketing in the USA.

While naming the product after yourself may seem egotistical and uncomfortable, it is very smart marketing. The consumer wants **someone** to sign off on the quality of what she eats and be responsible for it. Shade Tree Farm (a made-up example) could be a front for a multi-national food conglomerate for all she knows.

> *The consumer wants someone to sign off on the quality of what he or she eats, and to be responsible for it.*

Many consumers have discovered this about their favorite niche-market beers and this immediately destroyed their carefully crafted cachet. In a world of conglomeration, today's consumer is increasingly concerned with authenticity. They want your marketing

> *The LeRaysville Cheese Factory in LeRaysville, Pennsylvania markets its Sommelier cheese under four different names.*
>
> *A local artist designed a French label for the New York market and sold it as Sommelier.*
>
> *For the Portugese, under a private label named for their company, it is called Triumpho.*
>
> *A local customer suggested it be called Udder Delight with a cow's face on the label — the best selling version.*
>
> *The Russians call it Baltic Cream.*

story to be real. Naming your products after yourself also assures a cushy, highly paid, public relations job for yourself if you later decide to sell out to a conglomerate or go public. It could possibly add a royalty stream to your family for many generations. You may laugh at this idea now, but becoming a brand name offers excellent job protection.

In the corporate world an entrepreneur's job is considered over once he has developed a product and identified a viable niche. Many company founders are shocked to find that they are the first person canned after a buy-out. Think ahead!

BRAND YOUR PRODUCT

If your life's goal is to just live a pleasant life in the country, I would urge you to stay away from the wholesale trade. The Joel Salatin model while seemingly volume-limiting is actually far more feasible for most people than selling through the traditional supermarket due to the capital it requires for financing receivables. However, if your goal is to make multi-millions, a branded food product is one of the best ways to go. Small branded food product companies are the darlings of venture capitalists, particularly if they can be certified organic. As we will discuss, a new consumer market is where the big money is made. Currently, organic food products are the only food product group that is growing rapidly.

Even traditional supermarkets are likely to have organic food sections in the future. While this is good in that it dramatically expands the market, it may be bad for small organic producers who have had a local market monopoly.

With common specs and standards, organic foods will be increasingly "commodified." This will narrow the wide production margins organic producers currently enjoy and require larger production units. Remember, the larger the market becomes, the more the unfair advantage shifts to the larger sized production unit.

There is a good chance the current "natural" non-organic, meat products will be unable to attract many supermarkets' attention once national organic certification becomes available. Supermarkets in the future will have traditional and organic sections and products will have to fit one or the other. For potential customers to find grassfed beef, it will probably have to be in the organic section.

> *Farmland Black Angus Beef sold $100 million worth of beef in 1999. This is considered peanuts in the multi-billion dollar American beef business. However, Black Angus's net profit on this small amount exceeded that of America's three largest meat packers combined. Chief executive, John Miller, said the profit margin on Black Angus is 20 percent better than on their no-name commodity beef.*
>
> ***Forbes***

63

A Few Definitions

Organic—*subject to national standards of verification by organic certifying agencies. Check http:// www.ams.usda.gov/nop for the most up to date information.*

Processed foods—*may fall under FDA nutritional labeling requirements. What qualifies as "processed" varies by each state's definition.*

Meat, poultry or dairy products subject to state or federal inspection—*regulations may control the use of certain terms.*

Eco-labeling—*a method of informing the consumer about special environmental attributes under which your livestock were raised. Examples—water quality, animal welfare, food safety. A subjective value of eco-labeling is reaching consumers who have these same environmental concerns.*

Natural—*can only be applied to products with no artificial ingredients, colors, dyes, or preservatives and is only minimally processed (defined as smoked, roasted, frozen, dried, or fermented). Ground meat or the separation of egg yolks from the albumen is also considered minimal processing since this does not fundamentally alter the raw product.*

Free range—*chickens that are "cage free." The "range" of free-range definitions varies considerably.*

LABELED BEEF PROGRAMS IN FRANCE

The old saying about it being an ill wind that doesn't blow someone some good was certainly verified in 2001 by the "Mad Cow" (BSE) crisis in France. While total beef consumption in France plummeted by 25 percent, sales and prices of organic and labeled beef actually rose. "Our beef sales dropped by 50 percent the first day of the crisis," explained Mark Gambarotto of the beef packing company FQRN in St. Lo, Normandy. Less than a month later they were only down 25 percent.

> *The only small farmers doing well in France today are those who concentrate on producing high quality products that can be labeled and sold for a premium price.*
>
> **Mme. Fauqué**

While his company is primarily oriented toward commodity beef it also kills and labels animals for 5500 breeders of Normande dual-purpose cattle in his region.

"Our Normande labeled beef fully recovered its price and volume and is actually gaining market share daily against commodity beef." The Normande label's specifications are verified under the Certificate of Conformity–one of four labeling programs the French government had set up to promote and preserve French food quality and regional distinctiveness. Luckily it had been approved prior to the first BSE scare in 1996. The 2001 crisis in England provided a greater growth spurt.

> *The French consumer is very concerned about how animals are raised. They don't blindly trust anyone. They want verification.*
>
> **Mark Gambarotto**

THE CERTIFICATE OF CONFORMITY guarantees that the product was raised in a natural, non-industrial way. For example, the Normande label requires at least six months on pasture each year and guarantees that no GMOs or artificial hormones were used in its production. A minimum age of slaughter is set at 30 months for steers to discourage the use of grain feeding. A minimum of 12 days of aging is also required. The producers who pay for the program are subject to two inspections each year. One is announced and one is a surprise to insure conformity. Producers found out of conformity are denied from ever being able to participate in any premium-priced label for the rest of their lives. This threat is enough to ensure compliance.

> *"Fermier" certifies that everything sold on the farm was produced on the farm.*

PRESERVING REGIONAL SPECIALTIES.

Mme. Fauqué of the French Ministry of Agriculture said the French government first became interested in an organized labeling program in the early 1960s as a way to preserve regional food specialties. This resulted in the AOC which allows for a label that recognizes a regionally significant production technique that produces a unique taste. This is probably most familiar to Americans as the law that reserves the use of the word "Champagne" for sparkling wine produced in France's Champagne region and prevents its use elsewhere in France and the world. The AOC

> *In none of the European Union food regulations is the taste of the food discussed, but in France, the way the food tastes is everything.*
>
> **Mme. Fauqué**

certification is also widely used for French cheese.

Mme. Fauqué said the government hires professional taste testers who can differentiate the subtleties in
regional production. To earn an AOC or Label Rouge
classification a product has to go through a taste test of
60 dis-interested consumers. These consumers then are
offered the proposed product, a standard commodity
product, and a store label brand to taste. If the proposed
new labeled product does not taste significantly better,
the label is denied.

The labeling program really picked up steam in
the mid 1990s when a series of food scares from the
industrial agriculture segment started French consumers
to search for a more
"natural" and therefore
"safe" food supply. The
term "industrial" in
France is a widely used
term for confinement
animal agriculture as well
as North American style broad-acre crop farming.

> *Taste is always the most important criteria in awarding a French label.*
>
> **Mme. Fauqué**

Other government-supervised labeling programs
are the Label Rouge, Organic and previously mentioned
Certificate of Conformity.

LABEL ROUGE is a government-owned brand
that specifies non-industrial production methods. It is a
major free-range poultry brand in France. However,
there are also Label Rouges for beef and such unusual
items as hay and lawn grass seed.

The three criteria used for beef are taste, tenderness and degree of maturity (hard bones). While the
Anglo tradition is for young, early maturing breeds, the
French prefer slow maturing large-framed breeds due to
their better beef flavor. Beef is France's most variable
labeled product as the flavor changes with the seasons.

FARMSTEAD LABEL. There is also a separate label reserved for farmstead producers. This is the "fermier" label. This certifies that everything sold on the farm was produced on the farm.

All French food labels must also be approved by the strong National Consumers Union to prevent industrial food companies from trying to sneak a food item into the market place with a non-industrial label. There is already a major problem with the large companies trying to make their products physically resemble the non-industrial products to gain a better price.

Currently, Mme. Fauqué said all four labels earn at least a 10 to 30 percent price premium over commodity production. Thanks to the BSE crisis organic beef sold for 100 percent more than commodity beef at retail.

While labeled beef seems to have proven itself as an excellent insurance policy against a total market collapse, at least one Normande breeder complained that the majority of the market price premium of the labeled brands is being pocketed by the packer and the meat distributor.

"Of course, we farmers do it to ourselves," he said. "We are not interested in marketing. To make real money today requires the ability to both produce and seduce."

Richard and Peggy Sechrist of Fredericksburg, Texas said that getting their grassfed beef and chickens labeled organic instantly opened a lot of doors for their meat products in supermarkets.

They had previously tried a "Chemical Free" and "Natural" label with little result. They plan to keep selling some of their meat direct to consumers because it keeps them in direct contact with the feedback of consumers and satisfies their vision of creating local food security.

In culturally conservative areas like the South, a marketing approach based upon traditional values can be effective. Jane Bigger of Gold Hill, North Carolina, sells her grassfed beef, pork, eggs and chicken under the Yesterways Farm label. She chose the name to call attention to her traditional Southern production methods. She said these reflect a "tried and proven way of life."

Salad Bar Beef piques curiosity. The words were carefully chosen to stimulate conversation and educate customers. An educated patron is a loyal patron.

Joel Salatin

Near Thanksgiving, Rich Green delayed dressing out some pastured broilers. The Cornish Cross birds were so huge he called them Holiday Giants, Chickens with Cleavage. They sold in just a few days.

Joel Salatin

Forget the generic. Launch out into the world of designer language.

Joel Salatin.

How Much Should You Charge?

Want a handy formula for making a profit? Well, here it is:

Profit = volume x price - costs

The three variables we have to work with are volume (sales), price and costs. Which of these three has the greatest impact on profit? Let's take a look.

"Get bigger or get out" has been the mantra of modern agriculture for the last 40 years. Unfortunately, increasing volume is the least profitable approach. Here's why.

The average commodity beef rancher in the United States only nets between three percent and ten percent on a dollar of sales. This means an increased dollar of sales only brings three to ten cents down to the bottom line. The more profitable commodity ranchers are almost always the ones who have achieved financial maturity (low or no debt), a reasonable level of volume, and have low land costs per unit of production. Low land costs are primarily achieved via marriage, inheritance or leasing.

> *True businesses are cost-based pricing systems. The tools you need to manipulate are price, volume, and costs.*

Unfortunately, the lower end of rancher returns

70

is below the cost of capital. The cost of capital is considered to be the interest rate of the 30 year USA Treasury bond. This return is considered to be risk free and is the measuring post for all economic enterprises. Low, but

> *Cutting a dollar of expense is worth ten times as much as an extra dollar of production.*

positive returns allow mature, debt-free operations to continue to operate but effectively keep poorly capitalized participants out.

What about costs?

Ah, here we get a much higher return. A dollar of cost reduction drops a dollar straight to the bottom line and is a one-to-one relationship. However, there are two kinds of costs—fixed costs and variable costs—and most farmers and ranchers only concentrate on variable costs.

Variable costs are those directly tied to the enterprise. In other words, if you stopped doing a particular enterprise all the variable costs would also stop. Unfortunately, the majority of costs in ranching are fixed costs. The two biggest of which are land and machinery.

Much of the push to higher volume has been an effort to try to lower fixed costs by spreading them over more sales. This is never as effective as an actual cost cut because increased volume always increases direct costs, and more importantly, management costs.

> *It takes as much time and management effort to cut a small cost as it does to cut a big one.*
> **Peter Drucker**

Cost reduction through volume is always a Ushaped curve. What turns the cost line back up is the necessity to hire more management, and management compared to casual labor is very expensive. This is why the least-cost producer of any commodity will always be the owner-operator.

> *It pays to be expensive if your production is small.*

Peter Drucker said that when you try to improve profitability via cost control—concentrate on your biggest cost first. For example, you can fiddle around with trying to get your minerals for a dollar a bag cheaper forever and it won't make a significant difference in your bottom line.

However, if you spend all of your time trying to figure ways to cut your cow wintering costs the payoff to your management effort will be large. Cow wintering costs are typically 70 percent of total out-of-pocket costs. An even better cost control is the selling off of seldom used machinery and low productivity land as this would lower your fixed costs.

The secret to a high level of productivity is to concentrate your efforts where you get the biggest bang per bucket of sweat.

And what about price?

Now here's where life starts to get exciting. McKinsey Consulting's research found a one percent increase in the price of what you sell typically increases your net return by 12 percent! Talk about a bang for your effort!

> *Price and sales volume are opposite ends of the teeter-totter.*

Of course, this one to 12 ratio assumes no drop in sales or increase in costs, but it clearly shows that the majority of your effort should be spent in trying to sell what you produce for more.

(To figure your own level of response to price take one percent of your net sales and divide it by your net income.)

> *The trade-off of volume for margin is the heart of niche marketing.*

Unfortunately, commodity producers can't set their price. As we saw in the 1998 pork price collapse, the best producers and marketers could do nothing in the face of a massive price collapse. Commodity marketing is at best a system of trying to make the best of a potentially very bad situation. Commodities are defined as a price-based costing system. The price and specifications are set by the buyer and it is up to the producer to

> *Niche marketers can thrive as long as they do not grow their niches to the point where volume producers are attracted to them.*

meet both of these. Now here is a very uncomfortable question. If you can't control the price, can't control the specifications and—frequently as in dairy—when you produce it, are you really in business for yourself?

True businesses are cost-based pricing systems and you have all three tools—price, volume, costs— available for your manipulation. This makes them much more responsive to management input and in particular to marketing skills. If price goes up, sales volume goes down but not always in a straight-line, one-to-one ratio. According to McKinsey Consulting a 20 percent increase in price increases

> *In a niche market, small is indeed beautiful.*

profitability as long as sales do not drop more than 33 percent. Serving a small market also protects you from large, well-capitalized competitors. Big companies with big overheads (fixed costs) cannot serve small markets. This allows small businesses to co-exist with the big boys as long as they stay in small volume markets. However, being small and being poor are not synonymous. Small businesses can make excellent incomes as long as they target markets where they can sell their production at higher than normal prices. In other words, you can have a small volume of unit sales and be very profitable as long as you have a big margin in each unit.

> *Whether you have a thousand animals or ten the greatest return to your management effort will be in learning and working toward a system that will allow you to set your own price for what you produce.*

THE KNOWLEDGE BASED ECONOMY

In the pre-industrial economy, wealth was directly tied to land ownership because land was the limiting resource in an agricultural economy. In the industrial economy, wealth flowed to those who had the financial wherewithal to build capital-intensive factories and railroads. In the industrial economy capital was the limiting resource. In today's economy, wealth is flowing to those who know something most people don't.

> *The way you gain knowledge is to have made a lot of mistakes and have survived.*

At no time in history has the return to pure knowledge been as great as it is today. Unfortunately, you can't buy knowledge off the shelf the way you could land or a machine

74

in the earlier eras.

David Vetter of The Grain Place in Marquette, Nebraska, told me the only reason organic food currently brings a premium price is because very few people have the production knowledge (and quality of land) required to produce it.

Organic production does not cost more to produce in terms of off-the-shelf capital inputs, but it requires an entirely different knowledge base than most farmers have today.

In other words, the current organic price premium is a "pure return to knowledge." A pure return to what you have in your head is the highest margin enterprise there is because there is absolutely no cost to you. Of course, eventually today's rare knowledge will

> *Dairyman David Wright has found that with direct marketing he can make as much profit from 20 cows as he was making from 180 when he was in the commodity milk business.*

be learned by enough people that the premium will be greatly reduced or perhaps eliminated. Just as in the commodity business you can never stop growing in production output, in the non-commodity business you can never stop growing in developing rare knowledge.

My emphasis is on the word "rare." Commonplace knowledge offers little to no value advantage in either commodity or non-commodity businesses. This is why you need to always pay particular attention to people making gobs of money doing unusual things.

Unfortunately, the "average" farmer or rancher does not want to try anything new until he has seen at least three other farmers in his community be successful with it first. This guarantees that the average farmer will never see a better than average price because all of the premium-price margins occur during the early non-commodity phase.

> *The sole purpose of a business is the creation of customers.*
>
> ***Peter Drucker***

Let's look at some price premiums innovative grass farmers and ranchers are earning today.

Grassfed "natural" beef is selling direct to the consumer for 80 to 100 percent more than grainfed beef.

Grassfed organic lamb is selling direct for 250 to 300 percent more than commodity lamb.

Farmstead organic cheese sold direct is bringing 700 to 1500 percent more than commodity milk.

Wholesale organic milk currently sells for 200 percent more than commodity milk.

Alabama dairyman, David Wright, sells his non-homogenized "natural" milk direct to the consumer for 300 percent more than he sells commodity milk to his co-op.

Now to get a sense of the potential difference in profitability over commodity production multiply all of these percentages by 12.

This is the kind of revolution a 300 percent increase in price received can produce. Think what a 700 to 1500 percent increase could do!

> *The skill with the highest return to pure knowledge is, has been, and will always be, marketing.*

Now here's the downer in all of this for most farmers and ranchers.

With the exception of organic milk which is a

commodity (and therefore will come down in price in the future) each and every one of the opportunities presented requires that you create a customer for your production.

We all want products seemingly custom designed solely for who we imagine ourselves to be. Marketing can make the commonplace rare by segmenting the audience and selectively selling attributes. Here's an example.

What's the difference on the California meat market between a lamb and a "Basque" lamb? The answer is about $30 or more. Of course, there is no actual difference and the $30 premium is a pure return to marketing.

This is why I am so excited about the continual discovery of human health benefits from eating grassfed products. These benefits cost us

> *Who wants a product designed for everybody? Nobody!*

nothing to produce but can make our products worth much more to the consumer than the commonplace commodity.

The bottom line of all of this discussion is I think you should farm to live and that you should farm so as to live abundantly.

HOW TO DETERMINE PRICE

Most people never consider profit when determining the price they will charge. They have a touching faith that if they price "competitively" and the product sells at all, it will be profitable. Wrong. The competitive price is usually set by the volume, least-cost producer. No start-up can ever compete head on with an established player and hope to win.

The price you charge will always be subjective. This means you must choose it. There are no hard and fast guidelines. After decades of trying, marketing researchers have not discovered a single reliable method of judging the optimum

> *The first rule of niche marketing is be expensive first.*

price. However, the first rule of niche marketing is **be expensive first.**

What you charge is the primary way the customer perceives the value of your product. Whatever price you initially charge will set the value of your product and you will find it very difficult to subsequently raise your price if you discover it is too low to make a profit. In contrast, if you later decide to increase volume by lowering your price, you will find no customer resistance.

It is this resistance to a rising price that makes most meat retailers loathe to lower the retail price of beef during periods of over-supply. They know they will catch heck when they have to raise it again once the glut is over.

The biggest weakness of the capitalist system is that it has never been able to find a painless way to deal with an oversupply of product. While price is an excellent rationer in periods of product shortage, it is not nearly as effective in stimulating new demand during periods of oversupply.

> *For premium prices, demand must exceed production.*

What is usually necessary is for some suppliers to be forced from the game. Until this happens, oversupply periods are painful for everyone. Watch that inventory!

For there to be a premium price, production must always be slightly less than market demand. With every product there is a level of production called "the crossover point" where supply exceeds demand and the product becomes priced like a commodity.

Commodities cannot push prices higher by cutting back production due to product substitution. There is a fixed price/value relationship with the commonplace. The highest price of one commodity is set by the lowest price of its competition. A commonplace ordinary product is very hard to differentiate from the commodity priced version. This is why it is easier to receive a premium price for something that is radically different.

What is really hard to comprehend is that the oversupply of any premium product

> *The maximum price of beef is set by the price of chicken.*

does not have to be large to completely collapse its price premium. It can be as little as one more animal than there is a customer for. As a result there is usually little to no warning of a market collapse.

Really big profits accrue only to those who start a niche or get in very early. The latecomers usually go home on a stretcher. A study of the registered cattle business can give you dozens of examples of this.

> *The secret to success (in direct meat marketing) is to develop some killer products for the end meats and find a way to sell the ground meat for a good price. If you will do those two things, selling the rest of the carcass is easy.*
>
> **Mark Keller**

Setting Your Price

Here's an exercise to work through for pricing your product:

1. Set a price that is your best judgement of what the price should be.

_____

2. Write down the highest possible price you think you could get away with.

_____

3. Choose a price that would represent an exceptional value to the consumer.

_____

4. Set a price that is either outrageously low or high.

_____

Now estimate sales at each of these four prices.

_____

_____

_____

_____

Try to find the price which obtains both maximum sales and maximum margins. Remember, profits result from margin X volume. In a niche market, margin is everything because volume is likely to be low.

Remember, you are offering a product with unique value, not the same thing that's found in grocery stores.

Know your profit margin. Pay attention to the amount you make after costs rather than the grocery store price for similar products.

PRICING FOR VOLUME AND LOCATION

Business has been defined as the art of trading margin for volume. As one goes up the other will go down. Joel Salatin said this is a lesson that many new direct marketers have yet to learn.

> *Most people prefer that the food they buy be priced on a unit basis rather than by the pound. For example, "Sunday Roast - $10" sells better than "Roast - $4.00 per pound."*

"I hear all the time about people selling pastured eggs for $3.00 a dozen, but how many do they sell? I guarantee, they won't be able to sell 40,000 dozen like we do for that price." (Joel sells his eggs for an average of $1.60 uncartoned on the farm to $1.75 in a carton.)

Joel said that pricing is the biggest problem for new direct marketers. A price that is too high will keep your sales level below that needed for your farm to be commercially viable. Joel estimated you will need a minimum of $80,000 to $100,000 in gross sales to be commercially viable.

"Every time you raise your price you put yourself in a smaller niche," he said.

Joel said marketers who were near large cities could get away with far higher prices than those in rural areas. "It depends upon the size and wealth of your patron pond. Selling everything you produce for a premium price requires a huge patron pond. If your

> *People equate quality with a premium price.*
> **Joel Salatin**

town is wealthy enough to have a BMW dealership, it can probably support a premium-priced direct marketer. If it doesn't, watch out!"

He said in an average income community a rule-of-thumb he uses is Wal-Mart's price plus 20 percent. He said you can fiddle with this price both ways depending upon the wealth and age of your community.

For example, the prices for his products on his farm in rural Virginia are considerably below those charged to urban customers in the upscale metropolitan areas near Washington, D.C.

"There are just not enough premium-price customers in rural areas. Trying to sell for a big price premium guarantees that you will always be too small to make a living." However, he said it is also a big mistake to be too cheap. People everywhere expect that there will be a slight premium over the supermarket price for farm-fresh foods. "You want a little price premium to create a sense of specialness. A premium price is a part of the mystique of farm fresh foods. People equate quality with a premium price."

> *Kim Knight and Stefan Wolf raise pastured pigs in Wickenburg, Arizona. They butcher the hogs at 225 pounds and sell it for $165 for a half or $330 for a whole. This price includes all processing but not smoking.*
>
> *Unable to sell by the cut because they use a custom abattoir, they promote the meat as "farm to family" and target large families in their area. In 1999, they sold 55 hogs this way.*

VOLUME BUYERS SOLVE PROBLEMS

Joel said customers willing to buy a half or a whole steer should be rewarded with a sizable price discount because they have just solved a lot of marketing problems for you.

Unfortunately, the number of people willing to do this (or capable due to lack of freezer space) is very limited. In order to get sales volume, you will need the ability to sell beef by the cut and therein starts the problem of inventory balancing. There is a lot more hamburger in a steer than ribeye steaks.

> *The biggest problem with niche marketing is that we don't have a McDonald's to sell our lower-end cuts to.*
>
> **Joel Salatin**

Joel said the secret to increased profitability from direct marketing is not in raising the price of the premium cuts in a steer above what they cost in the supermarket but in increasing the price you get for the lesser cuts.

For example, Joel said his direct-marketed grassfed steers when translated to a live weight basis gross him 93 cents a pound. This is not tremendously more than feeder cattle bring at the top of the cattle cycle.

Much more significant is the fact that his cull cows gross him 75 cents a pound—a sizable premium even in these days of high beef prices.

> *Charles Ritch of Hartselle, Alabama said he made the classic mistake of pricing his grassfed meats too low when he first started. When he later had to raise his prices he said he lost 90 percent of the customers he had created.*
>
> *"You set the value of what you produce by your initial price. No one gets mad if you subsequently lower your price but they sure don't like it if you have to raise it."*

Of course, the real kicker is that these prices for both steers and cull cows remain the same over the whole cattle cycle. "I don't increase my prices when commodity prices go up," he said. "At the high price period of the cycle, I just hang in there with everyone else. It is during the low price phase that direct marketing really shines." Joel said that the premium priced cuts in the supermarket were already high enough and didn't require a price premium to be very profitable. He said the real problem was with ground meat and chuck.

> *What would you do if your current offerings cost only one-third of what they cost today? They will some day soon.*
>
> **Kevin Kelley**

RECREATIONAL FOODS

In pricing your products you need to realize that there are two types of food. One, he described as "recreational" and the other as "every day" food.

Recreational foods are those that are generally eaten at holiday time. This includes turkey, geese, smoked hams, venison, Easter lamb, etc. He said these foods were relatively insensitive to high prices. "There's no price resistance to Thanksgiving dinner," he said. "You can raise your prices as high as you like."

> *If you don't tell consumers how to choose, they are either not going to choose, or they are going to choose based on the one thing they do understand: price.*
>
> **Sergio Zyman**

Joel has found a commercial custom meat smoker and consequently plans to greatly increase his turkey and pastured pork production for holiday sales. He also considers the high-end beef and pork cuts as "recreational food." He has no resistance to $18 a pound beef filet mignon or $10 a pound pork tenderloin.

"Where you run into price resistance is with the every day food items. Chicken, eggs and ground beef. What really kills you is the high processing cost on your ground beef." (Joel said he was paying $150 a head to get his beeves slaughtered in a USDA approved plant.)

This necessity of balancing your inventory sales is what derails most direct marketers.

"You need a diverse customer base in order to balance your inventory. You can't just sell to white table cloth restaurants and upscale consumers. You've got to have a hamburger and hot dog customer as well."

> *When you are trying to make more money, you are trying to grow. If you don't grow, you die.*
> **Sergio Zyman**

For example, he had to add hot dogs to his sales inventory in order to sell his surplus beef chuck, pork shoulder and pork fat. (The 60 percent beef, 40 percent pork hot dogs sell for $5.00 a pound.) Luckily, Sally Fallon and her Weston Price followers are helping with this problem of surplus pork fat by creating a market for old-style pork lard.

Joel currently has around 400 on-farm customers. He also sells to 35 to 40 restaurants, two health food stores, several hundred Farmers' Market customers, and 100 metropolitan buying clubs (consumer co-ops) in the northern Virginia suburbs of Washington.

To put the marketing problem facing rural beef direct marketers in perspective consider that this large customer base only consumes around fifty 1000-pound steers a year.

"Beef is tough to sell because it is a luxury food item," Joel said. "People ask me all the time how they can up their beef sales and I tell them to add pastured poultry. We have four poultry customers for every beef customer." (To give beef its due, those 50 steers net Joel about the same money as 10,000 pastured broilers or around $30,000.) "The easiest product to sell are eggs. They are minimally regulated, not very perishable and are a whole with no parts so there is no inventory balancing."

Enterprise stacking (chickens following cattle, etc.) not only dramatically raises the per acre profitability of your farm but also makes your marketing effort more efficient. "The big expense in marketing is in finding a customer. Once you've got one you want to load her wagon with as many food items as possible. People don't want to shop in a store that only has one food item."

Unfortunately, due to strict rural zoning laws in Virginia Joel said he couldn't sell other farmers' products through his on-farm store but that in areas of the country that allow this, such an arrangement would be ideal. To give his on-farm customers more product diversity Joel is adding tree fruits, grapes and vegetables to his farm's production mix.

Examples of Joel's prices:

Beef $1.95/lb a split half or $1.85/lb for whole carcass.
Lamb $4.00 a pound
Broilers $1.65 a pound
Spent hens $1.25 a pound
Hogs $2.05 a half. $2.00 whole
Turkey $1.95 a pound

Other Direct Marketers' Prices:

Quarter $1.95
Ground quarter 100-150 lbs $1.45
Split half 85-150 lbs $1.95 - $2.35
Half 170-300 lbs $1.85 - $3.60
Whole 350-600 lbs $1.75 - $3.60

STEAKS:
Filet mignon $10.95
Rib steak $5.99 - $9.47
NY strip $9.13
Top sirloin $4 - $6.53
T-bone $5.99 - $6.50
Cube steak $3 - $5.99
Flank steak $5.24
London broil $4.99
Grilling steaks $4
Chuck steak $4
Round steak $3 - $4

ROASTS:
Rib $6.50
Top round $4.50
Chuck $2 - $4.25
Bottom round $4
Sirloin tip $4
Rump $2.50 - $3.17
Arm $3.04
English $2.50

OTHER:
Cured smoked beef $6.99
Hamburger $2.25 - $4
Stew/Stir fry/ Fajita $2.50 - $4
Ground round $3.56
Polish sausage (pork added) $3
Brisket $3
Liver/heart/tongue $1.99 - $2
Soup bones $1- $1.19

Beef Prices Per Pound

Where to Sell

T raditionally Farmers' Markets have been an outlet for farmers to sell fresh apples, squash, and sweet corn. Entrepreneurs across the country are realizing that, besides these standard fruits and vegetable items, grass-finished beef, pork, and eggs are also snatched off the table by health conscious shoppers.

Joel Salatin and Dave Schafer are experienced graziers and direct marketers willing to share their experience with their peers.

BACKGROUND

VIRGINIA: Salatin has always been a firm believer in the importance of customers purchasing directly at the farm and has had no problem selling his pastured beef, pork, rabbit, and eggs from his Virginia backporch. So when he was approached about selling meat at the local Staunton, Virginia Farmers' Market he was a bit reluctant. He eventually agreed, reasoning that at the worst it would be an opportunity for his apprentices to gain some marketing savvy.

After three years, Salatin was finally convinced that the opportunities in Virginia exceeded what his farm can provide.

MISSOURI: Dave Schafer is involved with the Kansas City Farmers' Market in a big way. The bulk of his pastured poultry and grass-finished beef, lamb, and pork is marketed to regular customers at the market. Many graziers, like Schafer, who are farming in rural settings find direct marketing difficult. For Schafer the Farmers' Market has been one of several creative ways to overcome the rural setting of his Missouri homeplace.

SALESMANSHIP

VIRGINIA: Before the myriad of Polyface farm chickens have broken their peaceful slumber, signs of scattered activity are clear in the Salatin farmhouse. After a bit, Joel and his son, Daniel, shuffle out of the back door to finish their early morning market preparations.

They move to the pickup truck and examine its contents. A small chest freezer, light enough for two men to lift, sits packed full of meat. A chain secures it for its upcoming journey.

Two picnic coolers full of cartons of pastured eggs are the last item loaded and checked off the market "to do" list.

By 6:30 the Salatins have backed into their reserved spot at the open air market and are unpacking. Fifteen minutes later the extension cord from the freezer is plugged into a lightpole outlet, card tables are standing, tablecloths are unfurled, and the price displays sit carefully angled to catch the customers' eye.

Early morning foot traffic is usually the thickest of the day and eggs, beef, pork, and chicken are sold in the usual undulating spurts of an average morning.

Salatin senior cracks out a dark colored Polyface egg next to a pale yoked store-bought counterpart and draws out comments from passing observers. Salatin said, "When your child is sick what is the first thing you notice?" Among the small crowd even the slowest observer makes the obvious link between the vitality of the pastured egg and the tonelessness of the factory egg.

> *People love to learn things as they shop. Edu-tainment shopping is becoming big business.*
>
> **Joel Salatin**

Salatin has employed several visual comparisons to aid passersby in understanding the superiority of grassfed meats. He feels it is important to educate customers on the health benefits grassland agriculture gives to his products.

Store bought chicken and his pastured poultry were each slow cooked. The broth from each was then poured into clear pans for a comparison. The difference was obvious. Salatin said, "The store bought chicken broth was gray. It looked and acted like manure; our broth was like amber honey."

High quality store bought hamburger and the Salatins' Salad Bar Beef were also cooked side by side. When the fat was poured out, the grassfed beef had only 1/3 of the fat of the standard beef. "That is a simple but powerful demonstration," Salatin said.

A few people chuckle at the Salatin sign which states, "Our beef comes from cows that don't eat chicken poop!"

Other people scratch their head and ask, "What is pigaerator pork?"

Yet another obviously confused attendee asks his friend, "How do you pasteurize an egg?"

The slogans and conversations all serve their purpose and contribute to a profitable morning. By noon the truck is repacked, profits are totaled, the market manager percentage is paid, and the Salatin duo is driving home munching on the day's reward—hot apple turnovers from the booth down the row.

MISSOURI: Schafer believes that the most important aspect to market is a proper display. He said, "People need to be able to see what you have."

Inadequate displays were his big initial mistake. He has now discovered the "Polyfoam" company which sells three products he finds invaluable.

1. "Insul-Ice"—small plastic freezer packs, which look like real ice cubes.

2. Display boxes—Styrofoam displays designed specifically for frozen foods.

3. Shipping boxes—Styrofoam boxes with a 25 lb or 55 lb capacity. These are used to ship gift packages of meat 2-day FedEx across the country. Cryovac™ packaging is another important selling point.

Schafer adds that the vendor should display, "anything that has ever been written about you." He puts out newspaper articles and magazine clippings written about his farm. An instant

A crowd of people at a booth attracts an even bigger crowd. Schafer only opens his booth from 8 until 10. Previous customers are warned that if they are not there by 10 the meat will be sold to someone else. This assures that there are a lot of people milling at the booth, which makes it intriguing to pass-ersby.

For new customers, he likes to be sold out so that he can get them to order for his next market day visit. "It sure feels good to arrive at a Farmers' Market with 90 percent of your meat already sold," he said.

rapport is established when a customer realizes that a farmer is "famous."

WHAT SELLS: VOLUME

VIRGINIA: Salatin has found gross sales at the Virginia market to be evenly distributed between beef, pork, chicken and eggs. He is excited about a new angle on sausage. Until recently the only USDA inspected sausage label his butcher carried contained MSG, a major sales turnoff for his health conscious buyers. After some sleuthing, Salatin found a company that sells small amounts of non-MSG sausage mix.

> *Dogs are not the only ones who love grassfed bones. Chefs love them because they are higher yielding and more flavorful for special recipes.*

The KOCH company sells baggies of inspected mixes that come in four different flavors; each bag makes 25 lbs of sausage. Salatin instructed the butcher to cut as much of the beef into steaks as possible. Steaks sell better than roasts.

MISSOURI: The sales for Schafer at his Kansas City market are in a definite order of demand. Chicken sells best, pork second, followed by lamb, and beef last.

He asks the butcher to turn low grade cuts like round steak into small, closely trimmed, cubes, that are good for stews, stir fry, and kabobs. The butcher charges no extra fee for his extra knife work, but Schafer realizes an extra $2/lb profit from the process.

Lamb customers have often not known what to do with shoulder cuts, so now part of every shoulder is cut into at least 5 lbs of the cubes.

Schafer even sells bones. Restaurant chefs and customers notice the bones from his grassfed beef to be higher yielding for sauces and gravies and more flavorful than usual and are willing to pay a significant premium. The price on bones has jumped from $0.49/lb to $1.49/lb.

Schafer has also begun selling chest freezers. He

Schafer maintains a "scarcity mentality" by only putting a small amount of his inventory on display at a time. "If there is only one steak left in the cooler, it is snatched up very quickly," he said. "If there are a dozen, people may want to think about it."

buys them used and resells them for a bit more. He sells them to customers who want to buy more of his frozen meat but do not have room in their kitchen. He said, "Once they buy one they can not say they don't have the freezer space!"

PRICING

VIRGINIA: Salatin has also been learning to flex his prices to match market demands. Slowly price sheets have been modified.

The basic idea is simple economics, raise the prices of the most desirable cuts. For Salatin that means raising the price on already high priced items like filet and tenderloin. Pork tenderloin is now up to $10/lb. He said, "One of the problems with selling a whole pig by the cut is that it is not all tenderloin. If you base your price on supermarket inventory you will never be able to compete."

Salatin said, "Our Farmers' Market customers are high-quality seekers looking for the best, not bargains. They are not hamburger eaters. We joke that if you have to ask the price for tenderloin—you can not afford it. When customers want tenderloin they do not care about the price."

When asked if the price of lower grade cuts like hamburger have decreased to offset the other price increases, Salatin laughed and added, "No, they keep going up too."

MISSOURI: Schafer feels pricing is a critical area that needs to be understood by the market vendor.

He uses a rather elaborate formula, a gross margin analysis, to ensure he does not undervalue his efforts. The formula accounts for all costs: direct costs, the opportunity costs of the land, and labor and marketing. The desired percent on return is figured, for Schafer this is at least a 30% return, and then he works backward to establish the necessary base price.

> *David Schafer and Alice Dobbs sell 4/5 of their farm's production of grassfed beef, lamb, chicken, turkey and pork through the Kansas City Farmers' Market. However, they only go to the market ten times a year.*
>
> *They are able to do this because they have built a loyal customer base over many years of selling at the market. Since most of their meat is already spoken for when they arrive, they normally run out of meat in just two hours.*

Schafer feels that the lack of a gross margin analysis causes most beginners to underprice their products.

An additional dollar per chicken charge is tagged on poultry delivered to the Farmers' Market to compensate for the extra handling and freezer space, and to encourage customers to buy direct from the farm.

As a rule he figures that until a thorough cost analysis is computed marketers should add at least a $0.25/lb marketing fee to the base price of products.

OPPORTUNITY

VIRGINIA: As for the opportunity in the Virginia area, Salatin says, "We have not scratched the surface yet, I do not want to put a cap on the potential. Once we realized we could sell chicken, the poultry sales were going bananas."

The always busy Salatin realizes he might not have the time to turn the Farmers' Market into his "centerpiece." "Profit depends on your particular Farmers' Market," he said. "Our Staunton market is small. Volume of sales depend on how busy the market is. Some areas have six Farmers' Markets and you can take your pick. Andy Lee, in his book *Chicken Tractor*, says you can go some places and not sell anything."

Salatin said, "Two ladies who just started a Farmers' Market on Embassy Row in Washington D.C., recently contacted me. They told me that they do not have a single meat vendor; this is a market with 3,000 customers a day and a heavy ethnic attendance. If I had the time to go there, I think our sales would go nuts. That place would sell five times as much as our Staunton market."

MISSOURI: Schafer differs from many sellers because he only goes to the market once or maybe twice a month, depending on the season, and then only for two hours (a point of interest to those with limited time).

> *Schafer's sales rose dramatically once he started selling at the Farmers' Market.*

Sales do not suffer by such intermittent attendance because the next sale date is announced and a pre-order sign up sheet employed.

This sale by "reservation" is achieved in three ways:

1. An order blank sent out annually to all regular customers—price, quantity, and pick-up dates are listed.

2. Customers who sign up at the Farmers' Market booth ask Schafer to bring them a certain amount of meat on the next scheduled market date.

3. Customers call him up at the farm and pre-order food.

David Schafer and Alice Dobbs started direct marketing as a way to get a decent price for their grassfed lambs. They added pastured chickens and pigs in 1994. In 1996 they realized their meat sales were large enough to make a full-time living. "It was like having an epiphany," David said. "We suddenly realized we could quit our day jobs."

The Kansas City market has become an avenue to overcome the difficulty of direct marketing in rural areas. Schafer lives in the heart of Missouri farmland, ninety minutes from his biggest market, and has had to be creative in his direct marketing efforts.

"The Farmers' Market propelled me," Schafer said. "Our gross sales went up significantly after we started at the market. It is now 70% of our business. Before I was waiting for the customers to come to me. The first few times at the Farmers' Market was awkward; I just sat there and did not sell much. Slowly things got better." Now a single trip averages over $1,000 in sales.

TECHNICAL ASPECTS

Bureaucracy follows the farmer all the way to the market. Regulations on meat sales vary among states and individual Farmers' Markets although several general principles consistently apply.

1. All frozen meat must kept below zero F. A plug-in chest freezer usually suffices.

2. Eggs must be kept below 40 F. Picnic coolers and ice packs are commonly used. A thermometer should be used in each cooler.

3. The market master must approve the particular methods of storing and displaying the meats.

Further issues should be researched in state and federal regulation guides. (See Resources section.)

Salatin and Schafer both use Cryovak™ packaging, a see-through, vacuum sealed, cellophane product. Many butchers give farmers the option of using this packaging. Salatin and Schafer agree that the small premium the butcher charges for the packaging is offset by the

> *Graziers direct marketing are realizing the incredible potential in bringing their animals frozen and packaged to a Farmers' Market instead of live to the sale barn.*

increased sales appeal. Customers like to be able to see the meat, and the vacuum seal reduces freezer damage.

VIRGINIA: A personalized farm label is another important sales and regulation point. A label gives the farm name recognition and helps customers feel they are purchasing something special. This is vital for what Salatin terms a move to "designer" food. The butcher uses the labels provided by the farmer to print weights, cut identification, and any ingredients. Salatin says that getting labels can be expensive for the small vendor; usually several thousand have to be ordered at a time.

The Polyface label for sausage had to be approved by the USDA. Information on obtaining a USDA approved label is available at local extension offices. Salatin went straight to Washington, D.C. to get his regulatory consent. A mail-in process is also available.

Salatin's understanding of the labeling regulations is that no USDA label approval is necessary as long as the product is a raw food. A rib eye steak or a pork tenderloin would be considered a raw product but sausage containing various spices would be a processed food and would need USDA label approval.

Salatin recently discovered that the 90-492 federal regulatory exemption on farm processed poultry allows for retail sales at Farmers' Markets. This is a real breakthrough because chicken can be a major seller.

Eggs are a fairly unregulated food, usually a bit of labeling and grading will meet the standard. The market master should be consulted for any market or state specific requirements.

MISSOURI: Schafer says label choice depends on the image one intends to project. He buys generic labels to save on label printing and design costs. The label lists each cut name and the butcher simply checks off the appropriate box to identify the cut. He does have a separate label for ground meat. Ground meat is the cut of greatest quantity and the special label reminds customers of the difference between his grassfed meat and store-bought fare. The label simply states "Premium Ground Beef," an unregulated description.

In Missouri, Schafer must pay the Kansas City Health Department

> *Mark Keller of Fairfield, California has found that the best way to get a high price for ground meat is to cook it. Keller sells his organic beef hamburgers for six dollars a piece at San Francisco Bay area Farmers' Markets.*

a $70 annual fee for what he terms, "the privilege of being inspected." The "privilege" entails rather sporadic and unannounced inspections insuring that all meat is being kept at the proper temperature. Schafer was

> *Farmers' Markets are the sharp end of the marketing stick.*
> **Gregg Simonds**

the only meat vendor at the Kansas City Farmers' Market not previously exempt from regulation under a "grandfather" clause. Consequently he has had to learn the give and take needed to gain the inspectors' approval.

MORE ON FARMERS' MARKETS

Wearing overalls and a straw hat can increase your sales at a Farmers' Market according to marketing specialist, Jeff Ishee, who wrote the book on *Dynamic Farmers' Marketing: A Guide to Successfully Selling Your Farmers' Market Products*.

GOOD THEATER. "It pays to play the hick," Jeff said. "You need to look like the stereotype your customer is expecting. Always remember that at its most basic level a Farmers' Market is theater."

Jeff said there are now 2000 Farmers' Markets in the USA. This is a 40% increase in just two years and nationwide sales total $1.1 billion. His family sells pastured eggs, pastured pork, market garden green goods, berries and bakery products at the Staunton, Virginia, Farmers' Market.

As previously pointed out, what you personally look like can have a big impact on your sales. An unkempt "hippie" look is a definite marketing disadvantage with Farmers' Market customers who tend to be upscale, middle-aged to elderly people. They expect a clean-cut, conservative appearance and a solicitous, respectful demeanor on the part of the vendor.

EARLY BIRDS. The typical Farmers' Market is open-air and seasonal. It is also typically an early morning business with most markets closing well before noon. "If you can't get up early, don't get into direct marketing," he warned.

LOCALLY PRODUCED. Jeff said it is important to emphasize that you are a local farmer and that your products are locally grown as well. 73% of your customers at a Farmers' Market will have traveled less than 10 miles. His customers like the idea of supporting local small-scale agriculture with their purchases. He said he builds a bigger support base by listing the local farm input suppliers he patronizes as well.

MARKETING ADVANTAGES WITH MEAT. At most Farmers' Markets, vegetables dominate and few people have meat, cheese or eggs for sale. Consequently, a producer who has these products has a definite marketing advantage.

He said with meat products, the most expensive cuts are the easiest to sell. He easily sells his pork tenderloin for $10 a lb. Hamburger is the hardest to sell and some producers price it as a come-on to attract new customers to their steaks and higher priced cuts.

At Farmers' Markets, market your farm as well as your products. Set up a poster display with photos, quotes from satisfied customers, calendar of events—processing/pick up dates, farm tours, open house. Have flyers available for customers to pick up. Include contact information, directions to the farm and a product list.

Pastured brown eggs are easy to sell at $1.25 to $3.50 a dozen and have no government regulations to meet. Consequently, pasture-raised brown eggs are an excellent product for a grazier to start direct marketing.

SHOW & TELL. With pasture-raised products, it is important to have photos displayed detailing the unique "clean and green" aspect of pasture produced products. People like to have a story to tell when they serve your product that adds to its uniqueness and cachet. Always, give it to them.

CAREFUL WITH YOUR CROPS. Jeff said it was important for small acreage farmers to stay away from any crops that can be picked with a machine. Small acreage farmers must concentrate on crops that require a lot of labor. For example, he sells raspberries, which must be hand-picked, for an amazing $48 a gallon.

ETHNIC SALES. Look for small ethnic markets that the large stores are overlooking and cater to them. For example, Alabama-native Ishee sells okra to other Deep South transplants for $4.00 a pound.

BE A SPECIALIST. A narrow range of products sells better than a wide range. "Let your customer know that you are a specialist. People feel more confident buying from a specialist. You will have much more credibility."

Mark Keller sells his organic tenderloin through Farmers' Markets in the Bay area for $26/lb. This price normally knocks people slightly off balance. Before they can regain enough composure to walk away he quickly adds, "There's a limit of four per customer." He has found that scarcity will overcome price objections nine times out of ten.

SIGNAGE. All advertising materials should look home-made and as non-slick as possible. For example, all signs should be hand written. However, be sure to read your signs from the customer's perspective before you post them.

> *Consider value-added products. Hotdogs made from low value trim and chuck sell for roughly the same price per pound as ribeye steak.*

Jeff said he put up a sign once that said "Pastured eggs by reservation only." He noticed an elderly lady reading and re-reading the sign. Finally she asked, "How do you get the chickens to lay eggs by reservation only?"

He said to always include signs telling of upcoming seasonal products that will soon be on sale and to put a "Sold Out" sign on any empty tray. "Nothing creates success like success. A sold out tray is an endorsement."

In conclusion, Jeff said that in a direct marketed farming operation the emphasis was on marketing rather than production. "It is 20% farming and 80% marketing," he said. "You don't have to be a highly skilled farmer to succeed."

FARMERS' MARKETS AND STANDS

* Andy Lee (author of *Backyard Market Gardening, The Entrepreneur's Guide to Selling What You Grow*) wears a name badge while working his booth at Farmer's Markets. In case potential customers don't notice the badge, he wears a woven straw hat to help people remember "the guy with the hat." He drops crushed basil into his pocket "so I'll smell like a farmer." He also plays music (use a tape player, radio, or even a live performer) to subtly draw people to his booth.

* Lee recommends keeping a log of each hour and the number of customers. The purpose of this is to reveal patterns of peak activity. Once you figure out your best hours for business, the log will no longer be necessary.

*You might try using the honor system for some products, such as eggs. (Set up a beach umbrella and keep them cool.)

* Keep flyers, business cards, catalogs, and order blanks available for buyers and browers.

* Use a notebook to jot down potential customer names and contacts to add to your mailing list. Offer to notify them when a seasonal product will be ready.

* To encourage repeat business, Andy Lee gives away a different recipe sheet each week.

* A price board will save your voice from answering the same questions over and over. Using a chalkboard or wipe-and-erase allows you to set down last-minute price adjustments after checking out prices offered by your competition. Markdowns are always welcome, but customers have a hard time swallowing markups.

* Fire up the Crockpot and offer free samples. Offer variety by cooking burgers, beef jerky, sliced brisket. Keep a stack of napkins handy and plenty of toothpicks for bite-size tasting. And don't forget a trash bin to keep your booth tidy.

> *Leianne Wright in Alabama set up an unattended table with a money jar beside the road to sell her crabapple jelly. No one ever stole a jar of jelly or money.*

* Demonstrations can attract customers. This can be particularly effective at a State Fair booth where

you could have a cow or goat to milk, spin or card wool, explain Argentine-style asado cooking.

* Don't be shy. When explaining the uniqueness of grassfed meats to a customer, speak just loud enough so that others nearby can eavesdrop on the conversation.

* Ron Macher in *Making Your Small Farm Profitable*, recommends checking out an event the year before you exhibit. This gives you a chance to talk with other exhibitors to get a sense of the time, effort and pay off in customer potential.

> *Andy Lee asks, "What else can I get for you?" opening the way for future products and sales.*

* For further details on working Farmers' Markets—from set up to selling to tear-down, read Andy Lee's *Backyard Market Gardening, The Entrepreneur's Guide to Selling What You Grow*. Many of his tips on marketing vegetables can be applied to meat products.

CUSTOMER SURVEYS

A survey of customers at three Northwest Farmers' Markets found that the presence of fresh pastured poultry would cause between 38 and 40 percent of them to shop the market more frequently.

Participating customers overwhelmingly were interested in pastured poultry and most indicated a preference towards parts over whole birds.

Greener Pastures Poultry is a collaboration between four family farms in Western Oregon. Under a unified label, Greener Pastures seeks to market premium pasture-raised poultry to restaurants and Farmers' Markets.

With a grant from SARE, Greener Pastures Poultry sought to develop a model for gauging the feasibility of using Farmers' Markets as a major outlet for marketing pastured poultry, as well as other fresh meats.

Dot Poster surveys were used to conduct customer surveys at three Farmers' Markets, with the goal of measuring the initial sales potential at the Farmers' Markets.

Dot Posters are a quick, unobtrusive means of surveying customer preferences and were developed by two Oregon State researchers. Each poster contains a single, carefully crafted question, and several specific responses. Customers are handed four stickers, and asked to place one on each poster "where it makes the most sense."

The On-Farm Store:

* David Wright, of Alexandria, Alabama found it would have been better to have built new rather than retrofit an existing building.

* For privacy's sake, locate your farm store on the highway end of the farm rather than near the house.

* Build for success rather than building something too small that you will quickly outgrow and end up having everything invested in an inadequately sized infrastructure.

* Another good location is a curbside stand at a country store. (Check insurance requirements for a road stand.)

* For details on how to turn your farm into a destination to lure customers, consult Ron Macher's *Making Your Small Farm Profitable*.

The response rate for each Farmers' Markets with a population count of 3,000 - 4,000 was nine percent; the weekday market surveyed had a participation rate of 30 percent, but only a population count of 1,500. The lower response at the busier markets may have been due to lack of booth staff.

Interestingly, while 60 to 70 percent of pastured poultry customers indicated they preferred to buy parts rather than whole chickens, 60 percent of actual sales were of whole chickens. This was probably due to the lack of supply of chicken parts.

The survey indicated that a pastured poultry producer could sell about 200 items at each market.

The fact that a sizable portion of those surveyed indicated that they would be more likely to shop at the Farmers' Market if this type of product was available, is important for a prospective Farmers' Market in making decisions about growth, or adding facilities for marketing fresh meats.

Other Places to Sell

* Church events.
* Civic clubs.
* Dinner theater.
* Booths at fall festivals, State Fairs, food festivals, 4th of July picnics, Living History events.
* Create your own on-farm event.

With each of these ideas, if you supply cooked meat products it is best if you do the cooking to control the quality of product for potential customers.

PROGRESSIONAL SALES MARKETING

Joel Salatin's family has four direct marketing methods:

1. ON THE FARM. Customers come to Polyface Farm to pick up their orders. "We live on a dirt road," he said. "You don't have to lock your car anytime except in August to keep the neighbors from putting zucchini squash in it when you're not looking."

2. FARMERS' MARKETS. "If you're the only one marketing meat at a Farmers' Market, you have a corner on the market," he said. "Farmers' Markets attract people who won't initially come to your farm. You have to have a handle, something distinctive to brand yourself."

3. THE BUYER'S LOCATION. He suggests going every other month to a certain location where a pool of buyers, such as those involved in an organic co-op or buyer's club, routinely pick up their orders. "It's like a drug deal," he said. "All the ordering is done by phone and mail. We're there and done within an hour. We get our money and we're gone."

If there are two drop-off points he will do both in the same day. All that's involved is transferring Polyface products from his coolers to theirs.

"Folks develop their own community. They're like a Polyface cheerleader club in the metro area. They purchase in volume at one place, one time, making things logistically suitable for the small farmer."

4. RESTAURANTS. Thursday is his delivery day, which works similar to the cooperative farmer delivery. "Once a year we bring the chefs out for a Chef's Appreciation Day. All the growers in our group prepare the food. We take them around on the hay wagon for a tour and serve them a meal. This deepens their loyalty."

Brian and Martha Goodsell of Candor, New York raise fallow deer, rabbits, chickens, turkeys, ducks and pheasants which they sell primarily to restaurants in New York's Finger Lakes region.

Martha said she learned early that making cold calls on restaurants is a big "don't." Chefs are busy people and just knocking on their door is sure to get your relationship off to a bad start. She said referrals from other restaurants are the best way to start a relationship.

METROPOLITAN BUYING CLUBS

I have been going to Joel Salatin's farm for 15 years and I have to get him to FAX me a map every time I go. I personally cannot think of a more incongruous place for a highly successful direct marketing farm to exist.

For many years, Joel required all of his customers to make the dusty journey to his farm to buy. Joel knew that what made a grocery store work was that the customer came to you. He had seen far too many farms go broke in the transportation business.

The sophisticated urban consumer is the best customer you can have. They are always willing to work with you. They seem to love to solve problems for you.

Joel Salatin

Washington, D.C. lies 125 miles northeast of Swoope. This city is the happy hunting ground of alternative food producers in the mid-Atlantic region. Several of these Washington alternative food buyers dutifully made the trek to Swoope to buy their food for years.

Joel said these were people who had become

> *David and Sue Remer of Remer Meats in Clinton, Missouri said a small town is an ideal place to retail meat because the competition is much less. David said a town of 10,000 people is large enough to support a retail meat store.*
>
> *Premium priced organic meat and the high dollar cuts tend to be difficult to sell to the older, less-educated consumers found in small town America. The Remers said that Wal-Mart is their biggest competitor. They try to price their meat slightly under them.*
>
> *Smoked meats are a good customer draw, and 30 percent of their meat is sold smoked.*
>
> *They sell both frozen and fresh meat and do not see any great discrimination against frozen meat. White butcher paper is far superior to vacuum packaging for the long term storage of frozen meat.*

disgusted with "corporate organic" foods available at the alternative food stores in suburban Washington. One customer told him that she had learned that the prettier the packaging the more compromised the food was. They were willing to go the distance to get "real food" but they kept telling Joel that they all had friends who wanted to buy his food but who were not going to drive 250 miles to do so. Wasn't there some way Joel could deliver his food to them?

Joel put a pencil to it and told them that if they and their friends would go together and order a minimum of $3000 he would deliver it to one agreed upon location. They could then come and pick up their orders near where they lived.

Thus was born Joel's first Metropolitan Buying Club. Today, some 100 Washington area customers buy their food from Joel in this way.

Here's how it works.

Most buying clubs start with a particularly enthusiastic customer who has somehow discovered Joel. Most of these people tend to know other people of similar food buying habits and so they become the catalyst for a buying club.

> *Most buying clubs start with a particularly enthusiastic customer.*

Twice a month Joel sends out a newsletter notifying past customers of what he has to offer and the prices. The customers then must FAX him their orders 24 hours prior to his scheduled delivery date.

This written order is very important for tax purposes because it establishes that the food was sold in Virginia even though it may be delivered in Maryland.

Joel meets the customers at a predetermined rendevous point. Most of these are at the house of the club organizer. However, one buying club's members are employees of a large Northern Virginia corporation and their delivery point is at their workplace.

These buying clubs quickly took off and soon became so big that Joel couldn't handle the deliveries and farm at the same time. He added a 20 cents a pound surcharge on the delivered food which allowed him to subcontract out the deliveries.

> *The key to success with a co-op is to keep it simple.*

In the early 20th century, dairymen had to find retail customers on their own. However, due to particular environmental advantages dairies tended to cluster in certain locales rather than being evenly spread over the countryside. This produced gross over-supply in one area and milk shortages in others. Large cities were particularly dairy deficient.

By pooling their milk into carload lots the

110

dairymen could use low-cost rail freight to ship their milk to the higher priced urban markets. This worked great as long as demand was in excess of supply. No one seemed to notice that a marketing co-op required a permanent staff and considerable permanent overhead investments that had to come out of the farmers' milk check.

However, the real problem was that the marketing staff was necessarily located near the urban customers and was far removed from the farmers. This created a major communications problem.

Marketers love to sell. With the urban markets swelling with immigrants, the urban marketers exhorted the dairy farmers to produce more.

Farmers love to produce. Freed of the responsibility of having to create a local customer for every quart of milk they produced, they became totally oriented toward increasing production. They made long-term fixed investments in silos and infrastructure based upon that day's milk price.

> *Problems occur when supply exceeds demand.*

Of course, this happy scenario only lasted while demand exceeded supply.

The major weakness of the capitalistic economy is that it doesn't have a painless way of dealing with product oversupply. Inventory in excess of sales always creates economic pain and is the root cause of economic recessions and depressions.

In Peter Senge's holistic business book, *The Fifth Discipline*, he describes how slight shortages in supply soon create massive increases in production.

For example, an urban retailer needs a couple of more quarts of milk a day but yells at the co-op for more milk because he doesn't want to miss a single sale.

111

The co-op yells at the farmer for more milk because they don't want a single disgruntled customer. The farmers respond by producing an additional tanker load of milk. Of course, this is far in excess of what the retailer wanted and so the price collapses.

> *In any buy/sell relationship the buyer has the most leverage.*

Unfortunately, once an increase in supply has been created bringing it back into balance with demand is a rather long-term process. One cannot turn cows off and on like a water spigot.

In fact, a spigot is an apt analogy for inventory balancing.

Senge said that supply balancing is like trying to adjust the temperature on a shower with a delay between when you turn the handle and when the water heats up or cools down. The longer the delay the more likely you are to be alternately scalded or frozen.

A marketing co-op, because it involves multiple suppliers in often remote areas and a far-removed marketing staff, is similar to a long-lag shower. It is almost inevitable that you will get burned.

TO CO-OPERATE OR NOT

The earliest modern farm co-operatives were "boxcar co-ops." Groups of small farmers would pool their money so they could order farm supplies, lime and fertilizer in carload lots.

At the turn of the century rail freight was a fraction of the cost of drayage and is still the lowest cost overland freight mode. Saving freight charges gave co-operative farmers a slight "unfair advantage" over non-co-operative farmers.

Usually the local County Agent held the farmers' money and accepted the responsibility of paying both the farm supplier and the railroad.

With the county agent seen as a trusted government employee, both the suppliers and the railroads felt comfortable that they would

> *The beauty of an owner-operator who markets his own production is that his communication chain is extremely short.*

be paid and readily shipped goods to faraway destinations with few questions.

In modern-day terms, Joel Salatin's Metropolitan Buying Clubs are similar to these boxcar co-ops in that they are buying pools designed to minimize freight (travel) on the part of both the customer and the farmer. Similar buying co-ops exist today for difficult to find organic supplies.

The key to success with these co-ops is that they are simple, single purpose, short-lived, have a good reputation for payment and have no continuing overhead or paid staff. They come into business, do their thing and then quickly go out of business.

The other early farm co-operative was the marketing co-op. Whereas the boxcar co-op was designed to facilitate buying, the marketing co-op was designed to facilitate selling.

How do such far removed players communicate?

> *Don't take on debt and infrastructure costs based upon early market premiums because they won't last.*

How do we fine-tune production to match daily market fluctuations? The only way the free market has found to communicate with producers is through price

113

changes, and yet marketing co-ops are typically formed under the premise that they will end the market price roller-coaster.

When an over-supply inevitably develops the moment of truth begins. We shared the good times, now how do we equitably share the bad times?

Who do you know who is willing to voluntarily cut back production so that his neighbors can continue to go full-bore?

What about the farmers' recent increase in debt

Pete Ferrell is a Kansas grazier who was a member of the now defunct Tallgrass Prairie Producer's Co-op. This was a co-op set up to market grassfed beef from the Flint Hills area of Kansas. He said the co-op made a big mistake when it entered the wholesale meat trade without doing the proper amount of homework first.

"The wholesale meat business is totally ruthless and cut throat. You are going to need a lot more capital than you think and you need to start out with experienced management. We made a lot of costly mistakes early on because we didn't know what we were doing," he said.

Ferrell said their biggest mistake was not having a suggested retail price for the meat. He said this was because they were afraid they might price the meat too high. As it turned out, the retailers priced it far higher than they dreamed it would ever sell for. This resulted in the retailer making a huge margin on each pound of beef he sold. This then became the margin he was accustomed to and didn't want to change to allow the co-op a greater share of the consumer's dollar.

"In retrospect, we should have hired a consultant who understood the natural meat trade. We learned the meat business the hard way–by doing it wrong," Ferrell said.

load for infrastructure to increase production on the bequest of the marketing people? The current problems are not of the farmers' making. Shouldn't the marketing people take all the pain?

Conversely, is the marketing staff willing to take a cut in pay so the farmers can continue to get a premium price for their production? What about the new office tower they just built? Why should they have to cut back so that a bunch of hayseeds they scarcely know won't have to? If the farmers hadn't gotten greedy and over-expanded, they wouldn't be in this mess. Shouldn't the farmers take all of the pain?

You know the answer.

In any buy/sell relationship the one doing the buying has the majority of the leverage. The only refuge for a seller is to try and find a kinder and gentler buyer somewhere else.

In the long-run, marketing co-ops can only thrive where they have total market hegemony. This is why they continually try to reduce their farmer members' marketing options by merging or purging their competitors out of business.

In the end, marketing co-ops that were started to expand a Farmer's Market inevitably wind up working to limit them. This is

> *Rule of thumb: always plan on a price five years in the future that is 30 percent lower than what you are currently receiving.*

because the co-op inevitably becomes a living thing in and of itself. Like any living thing, it is primarily interested in its own survival.

The beauty of an owner-operator who markets his own production is that his communication chain is extremely short. He can feel the water in his shower gradually changing and can avoid getting scalded.

This is not to say an owner-operator won't misjudge a market but when he does there is no time lost in recriminations about whose fault it is. He knows how to allocate the pain because the pain is all his.

Now, I know a lot of you will be asked to join and finance new marketing co-ops to develop new markets for grassfed meats and milk. If you are a large scale producer in a remote area, you may not have any choice if you want to participate in this market.

There could be several years of good prices for

Will and Jan Holder raise organic grassfed beef near Eagle Creek, Arizona and very early on learned not to listen to what people say but to watch what they do with their money.

"Everybody will agree that organic and family farming are great until there is money involved," Will said. "Suddenly, you'll find what you took for a huge demand shrinks down to a few very committed people."

They quickly realized they were going to have to sell their beef in Tucson and Phoenix, both a five- to six-hours drive away. They said driving so far to sell at a Farmers' Market wouldn't be cost-effective. They needed volume to make the transportation pay.

Toward that end they teamed up with a dozen other ranchers who were producing grassfed beef and formed a semi-cooperative called "Ervin's Natural Beef."

"We chose this way because it suited our particular set of circumstances," Will said. "That is the key, don't go into a situation 'knowing' your direction. Let demand and your strengths dictate that. Don't try to be all things to all people, look for a consumer demand that matches your strengths."

> *Sherry Haugen of Center, Colorado sells grassfed lamb to both restaurants and retail food stores. She sells it as regular lamb, pre-seasoned with a dry rub, Kibbee (ground lamb mixed with organic cracked wheat, egg, onion and garlic) and as prime cuts fresh or frozen. The lamb is processed to a "zero trim" fat level prior to sale and sold under her own USDA label.*
>
> *"Direct marketing is very time consuming but very definitely increases your income," Sherry said. "It is difficult to keep production time and marketing time balanced."*

co-op members but keep your feet on the ground. Don't take on debt and infrastructure costs based upon early market premiums because they won't last.

Use these early market premiums to make productivity investments that will allow you to continue to profit at lower prices.

Keep trying to develop your own personal markets and keep your costs low enough so that you can use the established commodity markets as a supply balancer. Be particularly careful about participating in a co-op with a species of livestock that does not have an alternative commodity market outlet.

If you only have one market outlet for your production, it is inevitable that you will eventually get squeezed. No, this is not just business. It is, however, human nature.

In conclusion, I believe that all the co-ops that truly work for the farmer are simple, single-purposed and short-lived. No business person has ever been able to completely transfer the marketing responsibility for their production to someone else, somewhere else and thrive in the long-run.

CATERED MEALS

Sandy Fisher said he was having a hard time building volume for his farm's organic grassfed beef, pastured chicken and vegetables in the Richmond, Virginia area. He was selling direct off the farm, through the local Farmers' Markets and wholesale to three area health food stores, yet sales were far below the production potential of his 600-acre farm.

"Richmond is a tough market for organics," he said. "Washington, D.C. and Maryland are much, much better."

While lacking a large sophisticated consumer market, one thing Richmond—as the state capitol— has plenty of is politics. While this might not seem a plus to some, political events almost always revolve around food. Fisher thought that selling his farm's products through catered dinner parties might be the way to get his farm's sales curve off dead center.

> *John Jamison of Latrobe, Pennsylvania said he converted his sheep farm to grassfed production after a couple of French chefs from nearby restaurants came to the farm and asked for grass-finished lambs. The farm now sells between 500 and 600 grassfinished lambs to white tablecloth restaurants each year.*
>
> *"Grassfed lamb was what they wanted and so that's what we did. It was all market driven," Jamison said.*

To get his catering business off the ground he recruited a local restaurant chef who was looking for something different than the daily grind of a fixed menu. Her name is Pam Hicks. Hicks stays busy catering political events from sit-down dinners to down-home barbecues. "We can cater parties of up to 600 people," she said. In addition to her catering duties, Hicks had started preparing pre-cooked meals

118

for sale through the farm's small on-farm store and deli. Reflecting the farm's pre-Civil War heritage, the store is located in a restored former brick slave cottage.

To keep aggravation at a minimum the store is only open on Saturdays. "Saturdays are a very busy day here," Fisher said. Currently the farm sells around 60 grassfed beeves through its various marketing venues each year.

> *New Zealand grassfed lamb has become the white tablecloth restaurant standard in the USA. This lamb is produced from animals which are eight months old and weigh 80 pounds. The lighter slaughter weight provides a perfectly sized plate portion which is important to restaurants.*

The beauty of many of the catered events is that they are heavy users of roasts and hamburger meat. Barbecues are particularly valuable because they use the brisket and other tough cuts that are particularly difficult to sell direct to the consumer. The farm currently has 200 beef cows so the production reserve for more grassfed sales is there.

Fisher said the farm was originally half crops and half grass but in 1985 cropping was discontinued and it became a beef-oriented grass farm. Today, it is all grass

> *Julie Matthews grazes sheep on Lopez Island, Washington, and sells her lambs direct to Seattle restaurants. She uses New Zealand sheep genetics exclusively because they have been selected to finish at 80 pounds (the restaurant standard) and to have good flavor.*

with the exception of a two acre organic market garden. Located in the Richmond suburbs the beautiful farm has been placed in a conservation reserve.

He first became interested in organic foods in 1987. His first move toward direct marketing was installing a small on-farm mill to produce organic wheat flour and corn meal. This mill still operates.

In 1996, he started direct marketing the farm's beef as organic grassfed. He recently added pastured broilers raised in movable shelters.

Fisher said the Farmers' Markets were the primary way they found new customers, the store was where the greatest margins were and the catering provided volume and consumed difficult-to-sell cuts. All in all, he said the farm had a direct customer base of around 1000 consumers.

SEASONALITY AND AVAILABILITY

David Wright of Wright Dairy in Alexandria, Alabama, found that his farm's buttermilk sales go down in the extremely hot periods in the summer because elderly people refuse to go out in the heat. Before he began manufacturing a premium ice cream on his farm,

---

Surveys of abattoirs in New Zealand have indicated that the primary factor influencing grassfed meat eating quality, functional properties and safety was the meat pH or acidity of the meat as measured 24 hours after death.

A low pH ensures consistency, eating quality and helps prevent spoilage. Stressed animals have low levels of glycogen in their muscles which prevents the pH from falling.

The New Zealand survey determined that this stress was more the result of on-farm practices than activities in and around the abattoir.

Pastured meat producers should cull their animals on temperament, have them familiar with being handled, have them fed well enough that they are gaining well, and make sure they are well fattened before sending them to slaughter.

he made up for this drop in buttermilk sales by adding a premium ice cream from a small farmstead plant in Mississippi that his younger customers loved.

David's research found ice cream manufacturing returns considerably more than cheese manufacturing on a per gallon of milk basis if one has an outlet for the butter-milk, which he does. The main problem is that ice cream is a highly seasonal product. Luckily cream (a byproduct of his buttermilk sales), can be frozen and used for the summer ice cream season. The two products naturally comple-ment each other.

> *Jim and LeeAnn VanDerPol raise pastured pigs and sheep near Kerkhoven, Minnesota. They started direct marketing by going to Farmers' Markets. They expanded their market-ing by having a sign-up sheet for those who would prefer their meat delivered to their homes on a regular basis. They had 10 customers sign up for this ser-vice in the first two weeks.*

In 2001, David donated all of his pastured poul-try equipment to a neighbor and now sells the eggs for him in his store. The pastured brown hen eggs are a hit with customers but too labor-intensive for a dairy-based direct marketer.

Ron Macher, editor of *Small Farm Today*, and author of *How to Make Your Small Farm Profitable* suggests that you plan to have your products available when others do not.

Grassfed meat products tend to frequently only be available in the fall of the year and few people can buy enough meat to last the whole year. The grazier who has meat for sale in the spring and summer can often easily attract away hard-won customers of the fall-only sup-plier. Have a good product, have it available in the fall as well, and you will probably keep them.

SPECIALTY MARKETS

"The most important rule of marketing is location, location, location," said Jan Moseley, of Texas Bison Company, based in the Blackland prairie of East Texas. "We had none of that. We lived on a gravel road, which was traveled mainly by local farmers."

> *Nugget Supermarkets said that the best way to break in at a supermarket is with a pre-wrapped specialty meat entree.*

That remote location didn't stop her from identifying and selling her bison to natural food stores, independents, meat markets, ethnic markets (a German deli), Farmers' Markets, convenience stores, restaurants, food shows, and the Internet. She made up a list of natural food stores from the Yellow Pages of the phone book and began making contacts.

Here's her advice on selling to food stores:

1. Think of yourself as a consultant rather than sales person. Your job is to help the store make sales.

2. First visit the stores to find out what their needs are. It can be to your advantage if they're already selling bison. This shows that they recognize the product and know it will sell. Never bad mouth other stores or products (such as grain-fed meats).

> *If you want to sell in upscale supermarkets, you need an attractive label that looks expensive.*

Simply put the emphasis on your product being grassfed and how that makes it different.

"The best education is going to stores to see how others are doing it. Look at a row of laundry

122

detergent. What's eye catching. What's not." She uses high contrast labels that stand out and are designed to attraction attention. "Never put a red or purple label on meat." Her labels have a UV finish that can be wiped clean.

3. Call the store manager, butcher or decision maker. Smiling while talking on the phone helps sales. Introduce yourself and make an appointment to meet. Don't start selling until you get there.

4. Make a good first impression. Jan wears a shirt with her name on it. "This gives the impression that my company has several employees who all wear similar uniforms." It also projects professionalism.

5. Realize that they are not only buying a product. "It's a relationship, like a marriage, that you work at for years."

6. When she meets the decision maker, she hands him or her a business card.

7. She brings samples of her best looking meat in an Igloo cooler.

8. She has Point-of-Purchase materials with her that explain the health advantages of grassfed meats.

Oakfield Grocery Store in California's Napa Valley is perhaps the country's ultimate dollar earning small rural grocery store. The tiny 850-square-foot store in a 100-year-old building specializes in fine wines, farmstead cheeses and European style processed and air-dried meats. It also has its own French-style bakery, coffee and expresso bar. In 2001, the store reportedly grossed four million dollars and netted two million.

But instead of showing it to them, she just lets them know it's available.

9. She has a list of references, which names other stores where her meat is available. If this is the first store you are approaching, give some history of how your meat products have sold through Farmers' Markets or on-farm sales. It's important to let the buyer know how long you've been in business and how long you plan to stay in business.

> *The average American eats about 30 pounds of ground beef a year. Ground beef contributes 45 percent of market sales of beef.*

10. Next she discusses how she packages her products. From trial and error she has learned that customers want bison in two or two and a half pound roasts. Patties and burgers are wrapped in single pound packaging. Smaller packages allow the customer to take a smaller risk on new or specialty meats, such as bison.

> *Yvonne and Craig Tucker of Choteau, Montana take their meat goats at weights between 60 and 70 pounds to a natural meat company. The carcasses are put through an Instant Quick Freeze unit and are shipped as halves or wholes to restaurants in the Pacific Northwest.*

11. All of her meat is USDA inspected and is sold frozen. She plans deliveries to stores every two weeks, but will make an extra run if a store sells out before that time.

12. Recipe cards are some of her Point-of-Purchase materials. One of the recipes came from a chef who uses her bison meat. His name and the restaurant's

name are listed on the card.

13. She uses white corrugated display boxes with her company name on them. When they run out of bison, her display boxes "reserve" her space in the meat counter.

> *Beef that has been aged loses the bright red color that some consumers prefer.*

14. The last thing she gives the decision maker is her price list. "By that point they are usually sold on the product."

15. "Do whatever is reasonable to help the store make sales." One thing she likes to do is stock the shelves. On delivery day she will dress as if she might work in the store and use that time to educate customers. "People come by and I'll ask, 'Do you eat bison? I eat it all the time. I'm so glad we stock it here. It just flies off the shelf." The first barrier to sales is a customer who wants to know how to cook it. In addition to recipes, she explains what it tastes like in her Point-of-Purchase materials.

16. Two or three times a year she does demonstrations in each of the stores where her bison meat is sold. She uses an electric skillet and fries up small patties.

> *Research at the University of Nebraska found that large beef cuts aged at 30° F required 15 days to reach the same level of tenderness as beef aged at 38° F for 11 to 12 days.*

Every half hour she'll wipe off the skillet to keep the demonstration looking clean. If traffic is low at the meat counter, she will put the patties on a plate and walk around the store. She explains to customers how she raises this bison not far from their community. Sales

125

jump every time she does a demo.

17. Finally, she offers a product guarantee. "If the product is sitting on the shelf too long it may not look good. I'll pull it as quickly as possible and that's what we'll have for dinner that night. It's not necessarily bad meat, just not attractive."

18. Jan has identified specialty markets for the hides, skulls, bladders, which results in an extra $300/ animal.

19. She has learned that maximizing sales to a store is more cost effective than having more stores. This helps minimize her transportation costs and time. "There's only so much bison a store can sell, but you can also sell them honey, eggs, or other farm products."

20. "Focus on what the store wants and show them how you can help them sell. Stick to the point, like a poem, not an essay. Then thank them for their time."

ETHNIC MARKETS

The population growth rate for ethnics in the United States far exceeds that of Anglos. The Hispanic market alone represents more than $100 billion in USA purchasing power, with African American and Asian markets close behind. Middle Eastern immigrants are making their presence felt too. In fact, surveys show

---

Bill and Anne Eaton of Moscow Hills, Missouri said that you must have patience to develop an ethnic trade. Realize that immigrants are very uncomfortable outside of their own community.

However, they found that if you can develop one ethnic customer a flood will follow.

---

that Islam is the fastest growing religion in the USA. With the exception of African Americans, all of these groups show a preference for mutton, lamb and goat over beef.

Goat meat marketers should be careful to not let their kids get over 80 pounds in weight. Today a 50 to 70 pound kid is ideal for most domestic marketing purposes. Muslims and Greeks are major customers for these heavier weight kids. It is important that these kids be visibly fleshy. On the other hand, Mexicans prefer a 25 to 40 pound kid which they call "cabrito."

France and Germany are complementary beef markets in that the French like the rump cuts and the Germans prefer their beef from the forequarters.

In North America, Mexicans and Anglos are similar complementary markets for the same reason. Anglos like the rump cuts and Mexicans like the forequarters.

Goat and lamb marketers need to keep in mind when major ethnic holidays occur. Every Muslim is required to eat goat or lamb during Ramadan. The second best time to sell goats and lamb is Greek Easter which occurs three weeks after traditional Easter.

Muslims prefer to kill their purchased animal on the farm by themselves, as their religion dictates. They will need to know where Northeast is (the direction of Mecca) and have a place to hang the animal for processing. Plastic bags should be provided for the offal. You should leave them alone while they conduct their prayers and slaughter their animal.

If you live in an area where ethnic communities are visible, they may have an ethnic Chamber of Commerce as well. These organizations will have market research on their communities and usually sponsor their communities' cultural festivals.

Large ethnic communities typically have their own newspapers and other media directed at their population. You can obtain these from the city's Chamber of Commerce.

A favorite menu item among Cubans and Ethiopians is half a sheep's head, stuffed and roasted complete with eyeballs, brains, nostrils and tongue. Lamb heads will be prized by ethnic restaurants serving these communities.

ETHNIC MARKETING PRIMER

Alice Valenzuela raises sheep, cattle and chickens in Sonora, Mexico. Prior to moving to Mexico she owned and operated a Hispanic community newspaper in San Francisco. Here are her tips on marketing to ethnic communities:

1. Establish a consistent presence in your customers' neighborhoods. Erect a food booth at the ethnic festivals held in your target community. Distribute your business cards and brochures there. Throughout the year, make sure your promotional materials are posted in areas frequented by these groups.

> *A visit to a local parish priest or mullah can give you valuable insights into your local ethnic communities.*

2. Be patient. Typically several months to a year will pass before you get any response to your efforts. Giving up too soon is the biggest mistake businesses make when trying to establish a presence in ethnic communities.

3. Develop cultural insight. Ethnic minorities

128

don't like to go where they don't feel welcome. One way to break through this resistance is to invite them to come in groups so they will feel safe.

4. Get rid of your cultural stereotypes. Ethnic minorities spend much more of their income on food than Anglos do. Do not think that ethnics are only customers for "cheap" cuts you can't sell to Anglos.

5. Don't forget that ethnics are proud to be American and want to be seen as American. Mexican Americans eat hamburgers as well as tacos. You must appeal to ethnics' cultural identity as well as their desire to be American. Always include some traditional "American" foods in your sales offering.

> *Here's an example of how immigrants are changing meat consumption patterns in the USA. If every goat currently alive in the USA was butchered, the meat from those goats could be consumed in the Philadelphia, Pennsylvania area in less than 30 days.*

Loading the Wagon

A drawback to niche marketing is that sooner rather than later you reach the limits of a narrow niche. You cannot cost-effectively change a person's mind with marketing efforts. I have people ask me for ammunition to fight vegetarians in their community. Forget about them! You will never be able to argue or advertise them into changing their mind.

You are seeking out people already pre-disposed to buy your product. You will discover most of these customers early on. Eventually, your sales curve will flatten out and each new customer will be much more expensive to find than the last.

The tendency is to try harder at what brought you early success. This seldom works. You have already gathered all of the easy to pick low-hanging fruit. Every new customer after this early group will come at an ever-increasing marketing expense and your margins will go to pot. The best way to deal with this sales plateau is to target new niches, or far better, come up with new products for your current customers.

A current customer is five times as profitable as a new customer.

In most instances the first sale to a customer

130

comes at a loss due to high marketing costs. It is only on that next sale that we make a profit. This is why all new businesses are unprofitable at first.

Marketing studies suggest a current customer is five times as profitable as a new customer. For example, one dairy

> *A new product should create a significant rush of customers early on.*

customer can be worth as much as $50,000 over a ten year time period.

Never try to broaden your appeal by modifying your current product to achieve a broader appeal. If you do, you will lose your current customers faster than you can attract new ones. Remember New Coke? Herein lies another trap for the unwary. A product can only occupy one peg in the customer's mind. It can only be one thing. For example, it cannot be both lean and fat. This does not mean you cannot produce and sell both products, but each product must have a different name and label and each will have a different consumer.

In effect, you are starting a new business within the business. In most instances, this new business should be someone else's responsibility to keep you from getting distracted. While a new business within a business may have some overhead cost advantages, a new product for a new niche is almost as risky as your

> *Beef jerky sales are estimated to be in excess of $860 million.*

first effort. It never pays to let a bird in the hand go to chase another one.

A major rule of marketing is that a new product should create a pretty significant rush of customers early on. If it doesn't, you probably have misread your market and you need to rethink it. It is far better to withdraw the product and reposition it than to continue to beat a dead horse.

This idea of selling multiple products to the same customer or customer profile is what Joel Salatin calls "loading the wagon." Don't be in just one thing. Have grass-finished beef **and** pastured poultry. Have eggs **and** rabbits. Have lots of

> *Leverage comes from selling more to the **same** consumer not in developing new products for different consumer niches.*

things you can sell the same customer, because it is extremely costly and difficult to get a new customer. In fact it is virtually impossible to make a profit if you have to generate a new customer for every product you produce.

A major reason mature companies are more profitable than startups is that they have a low market-ing cost, repeat customer base.

Remember, the leverage comes from selling more to the **same** consumer not in developing new products for different consumer niches. Developing a new consumer base is almost like starting a new busi-ness and almost invariably entails a significant period of losses due to high marketing expenses.

Another thing Joel did right (as you have read there are quite a few of them) was combining commod-ity and direct marketed production in his early stages of growth. He sorted the fat end of his commodity stocker steers for his premium priced grass-finished beef pro-gram, and sold the rest as feeder cattle. This allows for both volume and a premium price on some animals. This is a program more beef graziers interested in a grass-finished program need to consider.

I would challenge everyone considering a sizable grass-finished steer program to first do the following. Devise and implement a production system that will allow you to produce at least a truckload of 850 lb steers every month of the year. This will do two things. It will put you in the top one-third of the commodity market price and it will force you to think in terms of a planned series of forages rather than just one or two.

To be honest I have not seen anyone in North America pull this off yet. Every region has its production holes. Perhaps the most over-looked is the effect of heat on both fattening animals and the forages they consume. There was a very good reason why the King Ranch of Texas owned a summer "grass-fattening" ranch in the mountains of Pennsylvania. Our current year around supply of feeder cattle is dependent upon inter-regional specialization. I suspect a year around, grass-finished program will have to be as well. I hope you can prove me wrong.

Jim and Erika Kelly of Angel Camp Farms in Elgin, Minnesota give customers free eggs.

"Once they taste how good they are they start inquiring about our beef."

In addition to selling chicken, eggs, beef and pork, they also sell honey and apples from the farm.

Erika frequently gives free tours to school children and serves them Oreo cookies to remind them of their Belted Galloway cows.

They also hold a Customer Appreciation Barbecue each fall.

Kit and Kaboodle...Add on Sales

Linda and Verne Hubalek of Lindsborg, Kansas direct market bison meat from their Smoky Hill Bison Company. Through Internet sales their package bison meat products have reached customers as far away as New York and New England. Several Bison-related items educate and entertain buyers while adding creativity to their cash flow. Their goal is to generate an upbeat feeling about Kansas agriculture as well as sales outlets for their products.

*   * Bit-of-Bison Club. Bison lovers receive a poster of their adopted bison, bison biography, a bison book and a kit with bison fur and feed.*

*   * Farm Stock Photos. Digital photos of the farm and the animals (including bison) are sold through their Internet site, farmkansas.com.*

*   * Bison Box. Compiled with classrooms in mind, this box contains a Bison book, fact sheet, stuffed bison, food sample and patch of fur. Boxes are packed according to children's ages.*

*   * Harvest Box. Another classroom tool, this box packs samples of various grains along with miniature stuffed animals and a farming book.*

*   * Winter Robes, Salted Hides, Skulls.*

*   * Book Kansas! A catalog includes books on bison, Kansas, and Linda's fiction on pioneering life.*

SELLING ORGANIC MILK

Kerry and Barb Buchmayer of Brookfield, Missouri are running their own on-farm creamery. Their advice to other graziers seeking to add value to their milk by direct marketing fluid milk is to look before you leap. "Processing milk is a lot more fun to talk about than to do," Kerry said.

> *Supply balancing is the critical factor in direct marketing.*

"We thought assembling the equipment and building the plant was hard. But that has turned out to be the easy part. Selling the milk is what is hard."

The Buchmayers currently sell some 675 gallons of organic milk each week through some 40 to 50 stores in St. Louis, Kansas City and Iowa City, Iowa. The milk is priced between six and seven dollars a gallon at retail. It is both pasteurized and homogenized and sold in white plastic half gallon bottles as Green Hills Harvest Organic Milk.

The problem is that their premium-priced milk sales are only a fraction of the milk their herd of 60 mostly crossbred cows produces. The remainder of the milk is sold as heavily discounted Class C manufacturing milk. "Supply balancing is the critical factor in direct marketing," explained Barb Buchmayer. "The consumer

> *Prior to the 1930s, steers were frequently not slaughtered before five or six years of age, when they could weigh a ton or more.*
>
> *Fat or tallow was more valuable than the meat. One record steer weighed two tons.*

demand fluctuates from day to day, and with fresh milk you've got a highly perishable product. It has to go somewhere."

To add some stability, the Buchmayers started making their own butter. Butter is both storable and freezable whereas fresh milk isn't. Unfortunately, they do not yet have an outlet for the "real" buttermilk byproduct.

> *Having "produced locally on our family farm" on the label means more to most customers than organic certification.*

TASTE TEST. They found the best way to get their milk into stores is to give a sample of it to the store manager. "If your milk tastes good and they don't already have an organic milk product, you're usually in," Barb said. "Grocery store managers have all read the trade magazine stories about how fast organic is growing and they want more organic products for their stores."

BUYING FACTORS. She said her analysis was that their retail customers buy on four main factors: taste, organic, family farmer, locally produced. She said "Produced locally on our family farm" on their label is probably more important than the organic certification for most consumers. "Many customers I talk with don't even know what organic means."

ATTENTION TO DETAIL. She said that a premium priced product was held to higher standards than a commodity by its customers. Bottles that never leak and that are kept clean in the retail case are critical to sales. All of this attention to detail requires more labor and labor is what is lacking on many family farms today.

She said it requires two people to run the processing and bottling plant. They also have a fulltime delivery man and a part-time milker to help their son with the milking.

"An on-farm creamery would be ideal for a large extended family. You need lots of casual labor and that kind of labor is hard to pay for," Barb said.

AGGRESSIVE MARKETING. The high labor and plant investment means that the initial breakeven "nut" you have to cover is sizable. This means you have to hit the ground running with an aggressive marketing program from day one.

"I actually started selling milk before we had any product available," Barb said.

She said organic products sell best in high-income urban areas. Unfortunately, many stores will only sell one brand of organic milk. If Horizon Organic Milk is already in your target market, your marketing will be much more difficult. Still, the Buchmayers think being certified organic

Chuck and Tammy Benhoff of Farmville, Virginia raise ducks in movable pasture shelters similar to those used by many pastured chicken producers. Pastured ducks sell to restaurants in Charlottesville, Virginia for $4.00 per pound or around $20 per duck. The Benhoffs estimate they have around $5.00 total cost in each duck.

Ducks will need approximately twice the scald time as chickens due to their thick, oily feathers. Once properly scalded, ducks pluck easily.

is worth the trouble. "Organic is not a fad," Barb said. "Once customers are sold on the idea, they can't go back to a conventional product. Once they're educated, they can't close the door on you and go back."

Barb and Kerry admit that at times they are totally overwhelmed by the task they have taken on. However, they said direct marketing does offer some compensations. "I have had customers come up to me in the store and give me a big hug. They are so thankful for our milk," Barb said. "That's a wonderful experience you'll never get with a commodity dairy."

For an on-farm creamery they advise:

1. Get your pastures, dairy production techniques, and creamery skills up to speed before you start direct marketing your milk. Marketing will consume a large portion of your time once you start.

2. Be sure you are a people person. You have to be nice to people even when you don't feel like it. You have to be able to tell your story over and over without losing your enthusiasm.

3. You must have enough equity to self-finance a start-up. Lenders don't have confidence in new ideas.

David Phinney and Willow Smart's primary enterprise in Milton, Vermont is a sheep dairy, but cheese is not all they sell.

They sell certified organic lamb from the dairy's males, and organic Pork and Lamb Chorizo sausages are made from the pigs used to consume the dairy's whey and reject cheeses.

They also sell lambskins and wool blankets, which is another by-product of the dairy. The wool is carded, spun into yarn and woven at a family mill. The blankets sell for between $100 and $200. These blankets are sold through Farmers' Markets and over the Internet.

They recently added beef cattle to help break the sheep parasite cycle in their pastures.

4. You need to be in good physical health and young enough to still have a lot of personal energy. You cannot afford to hire the quality of labor you need to run a small creamery. In the early years, you will have to do this yourself.

5. You need to be mechanically inclined. In a creamery, things are always breaking.

6. You have to have an optimistic mindset and really believe in what you are doing. If you need the psychological support of your rural neighbors, don't do it. Many conventional farmers will be openly hostile to you if you go organic.

7. There are no vacations in the fluid milk business. It is a 52 week a year activity. If you want seasonal production and leisure time, concentrate on storable manufactured products like butter, cheese and ice cream.

8. Forget return on investment and six figure income predictions. Getting to breakeven as quickly as possible should be your only initial goal.

The Jeff and Karen Lubber family of Grand Rapids, Michigan raise and direct market pastured turkeys, chickens, pigs, sheep and beef cattle.

One of their daughters makes natural soaps and another makes candles from tallow and beeswax produced on the farm.

In addition, their son runs an on-farm bakery, which offers a variety of rolls, bread, scones and seasonal pies. The bakery's ingredients are organic and the flour is ground on-site in a stone grinder. Available for purchase is fresh-ground flour from a variety of grains.

The farm also has a state licensed poultry abattoir.

RENT A COW

The Stewardship Community near Loveland, Colorado, sells raw, unpasteurized Jersey milk to its members legally. Here's how. A customer buys a $20 share in a cow which yields approximately one gallon of milk per week. This is a one-time ownership fee and a customer may buy as many shares as she likes and can sell them back at any time. The customer also pays a $20 per month boarding fee for the cost of grass and milking the cows. David Lynch of the community said this marketing model has successfully faced many legal challenges and has never been over-ruled.

Thorough documentation of "ownership" of the animals with periodic newsletters on an animal's progress or activities can help justify the use of this method. Record keeping should also notify your customer of the unfortunate event if his animal should die.

Be aware that you may still be liable if someone becomes ill from the milk or meat you sold. As Neil Hamilton points out in *The Legal Guide for Direct Farm Marketing*, "you cannot control what your customers might do with the product once it leaves your farm."

Charles Ritch of Hartselle, Alabama said he realized that once you have developed a set of customers it is not necessary that you produce everything you sell to them.

Ritch said a locally made honey had done well and a neighbor raises pastured turkeys and pigs for him. He said he had also entered into a joint marketing agreement with an organic CSA vegetable farm near Birmingham.

"Our customers need vegetables. Their customers need meat and eggs. Its a win-win situation."

Brain and Martha Goodsell of Candor, New York graze 2000 fallow deer on their farm and sell the grassfed venison to area restaurants. They also have a small gift shop on their farm where local craftspeople who have used the farm's byproducts of antlers, leather, tallow, bones, hides and such to make buttons, peace-pipes, knife handles, gloves and purses can sell their wares.

FARMSTEAD CHEESE

You have to really be looking for Sweet Home Farm or you'll never find it. With just a small sign that says "Cheese For Sale" to indicate where to turn, Sweet Home Farm is located two miles from the paved highway on a dirt—not gravel—road in southernmost, rural Alabama near Elberta. It is hard to believe that thousands of people actually find their way here each year. But they do.

Despite its seemingly incongruous location, Sweet Home Farm is a national icon in farmstead cheese manufacturing. Winner of several national awards, prominently featured in the bible of

Customers are encouraged to sample the cheese before buying.

cheesemaking *The Cheese Primer* by Steven Jenkins and frequently written up by most of the major newspapers of the Deep South, Alyce Birchenough and Doug Wolbert who run Sweet Home Farm dismiss their fame with a smile and a shrug.

"We just like making cheese," Alyce said.

Their cheese odyssey started in 1978 when Alyce and Doug received a dairy cow as a wedding present. The cow's milk production was far more than they could drink, so Alyce started experimenting with

141

making cheese and butter for their own use.

"I had a degree in food and nutrition and was looking for a home-based business to get into," Alyce said. "For me farmstead cheese production was just a natural choice."

> *The more varieties of cheese you make the easier it will be to sell direct market from the farm.*

She said farmstead cheese is particularly attractive to women, not only because it is the highest paying rural job there is, but because it can be done without involving their husbands. "Women like something they can do on their own," she said.

After several years of dairying in Michigan, Alyce and Doug decided one particularly frozen day in 1984 that they had had enough of cold weather and high taxes and decided to look for a farm in the South. They chose Alabama because it has the lowest farm tax rate in the nation and because they knew some people there.

Armed with a soils map, Doug searched the Gulf Coast region for a small farm with extremely fertile soils and finally found a 30-acre farm near the small town of Elberta in Baldwin County. At the time of the farm's purchase, they

> *In upscale supermarkets, the normal markup for farmstead cheese and meats is 33 to 35 percent over wholesale.*

weren't concerned about the farm's out-of-the-way location because they planned to mail order all of their cheese production.

In 1986, Doug and Alyce started milking cows and in 1987 Alyce got her cheesemaking license from the state. Doug said the Deep South is good dairy country. The grass season is nearly year-round and the prices for dairy products are much higher than in the Midwest.

The big problem is that there is no supply infrastructure for cheese production. Everything they need has to be imported from the Midwest or Quebec.

TOO HOT FOR MAIL ORDER. They also quickly discovered that a mail order cheese operation was not going to work in a climate as hot as South Alabama's. They reoriented themselves toward serving a regional market drawn from an arc from New Orleans to Montgomery to Pensacola. Alyce said they sent press releases announcing their opening to their marketing area newspapers and, as Alyce remembers, "things just snowballed from there."

SOMETHING DIFFERENT. "The beautiful thing about a farmstead cheese operation in the South is that it is so unusual and rare the press absolutely loves it," Doug said. "The area newspapers will do a story and then come back and do it again every two years."

This free publicity and word of mouth from satisfied customers has been all the marketing necessary to sell the farm's annual production of 10,000 lbs of cheese.

The term artisanal or artisan cheesemaking describes the production of cheese by hand in small quantities in a way that respects the tradition of the cheese.

Farmstead cheese refers to cheese made using only the milk from a cheesemaker's own herd.

While Alyce said some farmstead cheeses do sell for as much as $15 a pound in urban area specialty cheese stores, she can't get those prices in rural Alabama. Her cheeses are priced from $7 to $9 a pound and sell well. Her Blue cheese she admits is "woefully underpriced" compared to urban market prices.

Joanna Gioja of Champaign, Illinois is only 16 but already milks 27 dairy goats from which she sells milk, soft and hard cheeses, yogurt, butter and ice cream. Male goats are sold to ethnic students at the large university in her town for meat. She also recently added hair sheep and pastured veal calves. These are sold live to her customers and are delivered to a local locker plant for them. Her siblings also raise poultry, ducks, geese, egg layers, turkeys and broilers. Busy family!

She can make about 120 lbs of cheese from 1000 lbs of Guernsey cow milk. This means that the milk is worth around $100 cwt. This allows a 20-cow dairy to produce what Alyce describes as the equivalent of a "doctor's wage."

START SLOW. However, she quickly adds that this doesn't mean that a person with a 200-cow dairy should think they are going to be able to sell all of their milk for such a high price. She said they should keep selling most of their milk as commodity milk and start making cheese on a very small scale with just a portion of their production.

"It is much better to grow by taking lots of little baby steps. I try to get people to think in the terms of 10 cow increments," she said.

"Artisanal cheesemaking has a very high labor input per unit of production. You need one body for every 10,000 lbs of cheese you make and that body can't also be milking the cows."

She said farmstead cheese manufacturing would be an ideal enterprise for a couple with children. "A lot of cheesemaking labor is babysitting," she said. "Older children would be an excellent labor source."

Alyce said they spent around $100,000 assembling their cheese manufacturing equipment and building their combination milking parlor/cheese plant/retail store. She said novice cheesemakers need to have an experienced cheesemaker help them because the equipment dealers will sell you more than you really need. They took their time and were able to assemble their complete plant from used equipment purchased in the Midwest.

THE GRASS FARM. Doug is in charge of the farm and milking. Currently he has 21 dairy cows (this includes raising replacements) and 16 beef cows on 60 acres of open pasture, half of which is allocated to the dairy cows.

He uses a bermudagrass base overseeded in the fall with annual ryegrass. He also likes Cherokee Red clover and Osceola white clover which he said work exceptionally well for him. Haymaking is done by a neighbor on shares. Locally obtained broiler litter is used for nitrogen and phosphate fertilization. His pastures are subdivided and rotational grazing is used. Doug said the farm is twice the size it needs to be because they bought out a chemical-farming neighbor to stop his chemical drift onto their pastures. These extra

Helen and Rick Feete of Galax, Virginia turn about ten percent of the milk their 75 head of Jerseys make into a farmstead cheese called Appalachian Jack. They sell their cheese through local natural food stores and Farmers' Markets. Between Thanksgiving and Christmas they hold open houses at their dairy for interested consumers. These open houses include cheese tastings and a holiday cheese board set up along with gift selections. As a seasonal dairy, they only milk once a day in December and dry all cows off on Christmas Eve.

acres are kept open by the herd of Guernsey/Angus cross beef cows. These high milking cows produce fat 600-pound calves, which are sold as baby beef to the local locker trade for a dollar a pound liveweight.

> *The real secret to successful farmstead cheese production is to make something no one else is making.*

After several years of using only purebred Guernsey cows, Doug now breeds them to Jersey bulls to get his cows' body phenotype smaller and more grass-friendly. He likes the Guernsey for its docility and high milk solid milk but feels the breed is getting increasingly hung up on the "bigger is better" syndrome.

WHEY PIGS. Doug and Alyce feed their whey (the liquid byproduct of cheesemaking) to their pastured pigs along with some garden scraps and corn. Taking away the pigs' water will increase their whey consumption. They also use pigs to glean their pecan orchard after harvest. They report these pecan-finished pigs have a "fabulous" taste.

> *If people want a cheese that tastes and looks the same all the time, they should buy factory-made cheese–not farmstead cheese.*

DUCKS FOR FLIES. Doug and Alyce get excellent fly control from free-ranging ducks. Just warn your customers that ducks do not like being held.

QUALITY CONTROL. Doug said they only produce their own milk as a quality control feature. "If we could buy milk of the same quality as we are producing, we would have a much easier life just buying milk and making cheese," he said.

Alyce disagreed. "To have a quality cheese it is absolutely necessary to control your raw ingredients. You need quality milk and you need good quality starter cultures. I personally like the total control we have with a grass-to-consumer product."

Alyce used to make cheese five days a week but now only makes it for three. After 15 years of making cheese she sometimes had to psyche herself up to get out of bed in the morning. "I lie there telling myself, 'I want to make cheese. I want to make cheese.'"

CELEBRATE WHAT YOU CAN'T CONTROL. She said making cheese from the milk of year-round pastured cows constantly required tweaking because the milk changed with the seasonal changes in the pasture sward. For example, cheese made in the spring when the clovers were plentiful tastes different and has a much yellower color than that made when the grasses are dominant.

Larry Swain, a community development specialist with the University of Wisconsin-River Falls, calculates that a 100-cow dairy investing $250,000 in a fluid processing plant and counting raw milk cost at $13 cwt can produce $200,000 in annual margin to service debt by selling just 600 gallons a day at $3.00 a gallon.

"Our motto is 'celebrate what you can't control.' If people want a cheese that tastes and looks the same all the time, they should buy factory-made cheese—not farmstead cheese," she said.

She has made non-pasteurized hard cheeses and pasteurized soft cheeses. Soft cheeses are the traditional standard on the Gulf Coast due to the heat. Non-pasteurized hard cheeses must be stored for 60 days at 59° F before they can legally be sold. Here's why:

As cheese ages it falls in pH. Bad bacteria cannot live in low pH cheese. The good bacteria that ripen the cheese can. The longer the cheese ages the sharper the flavor. The major constraint on increasing Sweet Home's cheese production is the lack of cooler space for aging.

VARIETY IS KEY. "We try to make a very high flavor cheese," Alyce said. "When you eat something with a lot of flavor you tend to eat less. That's why the French are not fat. Their food satisfies them more so they eat less of it than we do."

Alyce currently makes 16 different varieties of cheese. Her most popular is named Elberta after the town, and is from her own recipe developed at the farm.

Alan and Mary Yegerlehner of Clay City, Indiana allow their March-born dairy calves to stay on their mothers until mid-June. The calves gain well when weaned. Leaving the calves on the cows allows Alan and Mary to milk their Dutch Belt cows only once a day. The cows are fed no grain to keep the CLA level in the milk high.

Their milk is turned into cheese, ice cream and butter. Their cheese is tested for CLA content at Purdue University.

Cull cows become summer sausage, bologna, salami, pepperoni, hot dogs, and hamburgers.

The cheese whey is fed to pigs and they are marketed as halves or wholes, sausage, Bratwurst and pork chops.

The Yegerlehners market their cheese and meat products through two Farmers' Markets, an on-farm store and through a supermarket in Bloomington, Indiana. The cheese sells at a range of prices from $4.55 to $6.75 a pound. In 2001, they made 12,000 pounds of cheese.

"The real secret to successful farmstead cheese production is to make something no one else is making," she said. "The more varieties of cheese you know how to make the easier it will be to sell all of your production direct off the farm. If you make a lot of only one variety the marketing gets really risky. You will probably have to wholesale a good portion of your production and there goes your margin."

> *Specialty cheeses can turn low value fluid milk into a $140 cwt equivalent product at retail. The University of Wisconsin-Madison Center for Dairy Research has identified 1400 cheese varieties. "There's a world of opportunity out there," said Jim Path, a University of Wisconsin dairy scientist.*

Doug and Alyce also make farmstead butter which they sell as "Country Butter." They also used to sell goat cheese as well but found there was too little demand for it in the Deep South.

LIMITED STORE HOURS. The Sweet Home Farm Store is only open to the public Wednesday through Saturday. This is to allow Alyce time to make her cheese in peace and for she and Doug to have some private time. The gate to the farm is kept locked to show they mean it when they say they are CLOSED.

"The hardest thing on the farm for me to do is to sit out in the shop," Doug said. "Everybody wants something different. You have to know how to guide them."

In addition to their own dairy products they sell other organic products from nearby producers including a locally made organic peanut butter. Their average sale per customer is between $11 and $13.

Alyce said, "I find retailing a lot of fun. It keeps you socialized and makes you a part of the community."

SHOW AND TELL AND TASTE. Farmstead customers want to hear a story about the product they are buying and what makes it exceptional. Doug and Alyce have a photo series in the store that shows the various steps in cheese production. "Our customers arrive in everything from Jaguars to jalopies. The trip up the dirt road seems to make buying here more of an adventure. We haven't found the out-of-the-way location to be the problem we thought it would be."

Every customer is encouraged to sample the cheese before buying. This is the make-or-break point in any farmstead production. The customer loves the romance but the product had better taste exceptional as well. "'Proud and passionate sells itself' is our marketing slogan," Alyce said. "A taste of your product should sell it for you."

Louisiana dairyman, Henry Mauthe, remembered when he was a boy how fresh milk soured quickly from the heat making it almost impossible to sell. As a result, clabbered milk would be poured into cheesecloth and hung under the region's huge live oak trees to solidify into a soft cheese.

French Creoles regularly ate it on thick slices of French bread sprinkled with brown sugar for breakfast. Over time the local cheese picked up the name Creole cream cheese.

In the shift from small locally owned creameries to dairy co-op conglomerates, the local cream cheese was lost until Mauthe located 1000 of the traditional cheese molds and assembled the necessary equipment.

Today his 10-cow, grass-based, Jersey dairy produces and sells around 1400 containers of Creole cream cheese weekly. It is marketed in specialty food stores in New Orleans and at area Farmers' Markets.

Think You Want to Make Cheese?

Here are the steps Alyce Birchenough recommends a novice cheesemaker should follow:

1. Buy a book on how to make cheese at home. Try making some cheese on a very small scale and see if you like doing it. Visit with as many farmstead producers as possible. Identify other cheesemakers in your area. Will their products compete with yours?

*2. Take a university class on cheesemaking. Alyce went to the University of Guelph in Ontario and recommends it. She also recommends the **Small Dairy Resource Book** from Vicki Dunaway.*

3. Figure out your logistics. Are you going to buy or make your own milk? Are you going to have to learn a dairy grazier's skills as well as those of a cheesemaker?

4. Practice, practice, practice. You want to make all of your mistakes making cheese for your family—not your customers.

5. Choose a cheese you personally like to eat and can feel enthusiastic about. The type of cheese you decide to make will determine the type of equipment you need to buy. Try to make a cheese no one else in your area is making.

SUCKLED PASTURED VEAL

Rick Hopkins said the primary problem with marketing veal in the Midwest is that it seldom crosses consumers' minds. "Midwesterners don't expect to find veal, so they never think about it," he said. While veal sells for $22 a pound in New York, he hasn't been able to get anywhere near that kind of price in the Springfield, Missouri market.

> *Milk-fed veal is the meat from a calf usually one to three months of age. Veal obtained from calves a few days old is known as bob veal.*

Less than three percent of the USA population eats veal so it is very much a niche market. However, after three years he has developed a good client base for his veal product in southwestern Missouri.

The veal is sold under the brand name of Elysian Veal. This is a play on the Greek name for heaven—Elysian Fields.

Unlike most veal which is from male dairy calves, Hopkins' are from beef cows and the calves naturally suckle their mothers on pasture. This more humane production system has proven to be more acceptable to consumers—many of whom who had previously refused to buy cage-raised veal.

> *Milk-fed veal is lighter in color and generally more tender than the darker-colored veal produced from older, heavier, pasture-raised veal calves.*

The calves are weaned at 10 weeks of age when they typically weigh 225 to 250 pounds. Calves this size gross him $470 a head when direct marketed. At this retail sales price he nets $200 a calf.

He said if you are in the Northeast you can probably double his net.

The primary reason he started direct marketing was to get out of the cattle cycle and to allow himself to go ranching full-time. He chose veal production because it was the nearest thing production-wise to regular cow-calf.

An abattoir charges him $60 to process a calf. The meat is aged for four to five days and is sold frozen in clear plastic vacuum packaging.

He said they first started marketing by giving away meat to their friends who then returned to buy. He currently sells 61 percent of his veal at the Springfield Farmers' Market and the rest directly off his farm.

> *In the mid 1960s, Americans ate more than four times as much veal as they do today. This has been the greatest decline in per capita meat consumption for the past twenty-five years. Pictures of veal calves chained in tiny huts have definitely affected consumers' attitudes.*

A good seller for him is whole ground meat from 30-week-old unweaned steers which retails for $4.22 a pound.

He has discovered that customers are willing to pay to have all of their veal and beef boneless. "They're willing to pay more for less. They complain about the big bones in steaks."

He plans to discontinue selling veal sirloin steaks because most people don't know how to cook them. He said most people want to grill them like regular steaks and are disappointed with the result.

He said quality veal requires an extremely docile calf. Meat from an excited calf has an unpleasant "wild" taste. Also, he has found veal from heifer calves is tastier than that from bull calves.

Hopkins has found that 10 weeks of age is when the veal starts to shift from pink to red. As a result, he wants a calf that has the genetics to gain rapidly early in its life. After much breed experimentation he has settled on the Beefmaster breed.

The bulls are run with the cows at all times to spread out the calving season for marketing purposes. This practice in conjunction with the short lactation allows some cows to have more than one calf in any given 365-day period.

MORE PRODUCTS

Like most direct marketers he discovered that it is far easier to sell more to an existing customer than to find a new customer. He added lamb to his sales because his customers asked for it.

He buys these from a local grazier, slaughters and resells them for a profit of $60 a head. He said he could net $140 a lamb on home-raised ones.

In North America, old beef was the type that would be eaten most frequently until the late 1930s. This beef was primarily from oxen or cows that often worked hard or delivered many calves before they were finally slaughtered. Cooks dealt with this toughness by marinating steaks in clarified butter or a vinegar and wine mixture, pounding and tenderizing, or simmering for several hours in red wine. Veal was usually only available in the spring.

Historic and Endangered Livestock and Poultry Breeds

He would like to offer goat meat as well but currently the goats in his area cost too much for him to make a profit re-selling them and his fences aren't good enough to raise them.

He said the big limiting factor in direct marketing goats is that there is not much of a "white collar" market for them and this limits their upside sales price.

He said a grazier in his area could net nearly $100 more on a direct-marketed lamb than on a goat.

Recently, he has added "French-style Beef" from 36-month-old, open cows and has found good acceptance from his customers. Surprisingly, the roasts from these older animals are what people most rave about. Also, he has had no problem selling the ground beef.

Tom and Tracey Delehanty of Socorro, New Mexico run the largest certified organic, pastured poultry operation in the USA at around 1200 chickens per week.

His marketing strategy is to educate consumers, stores and restaurants about the pastured poultry production model and its benefit to the soil and environment.

Tom's chickens are currently being sold by a marketing co-op in seven to eight Southwestern Farmers' Markets throughout the summer.

He hopes to eventually build a USDA approved processing plant and go to 25,000 chickens a week.

As with veal, it is the sirloin steaks that are his slow sellers and for the same reason. People try to grill them like a ribeye and are disappointed. He plans to discontinue the cut.

He said he didn't sell halves and wholes because he thought there was too much risk in it. "If I've got one dissatisfied customer with a whole cow, what am I going to do with that cow?"

However, in reality, dissatisfaction hasn't been much of a problem. In his three years in business he has only had three customers complain.

His three-year-old open cows sell for $1400 at retail and net him around $1100 a head. He said he thinks he can sell 36-month-old steers for $1500.

He said graziers trying to sell very lean, young beef would not be able to compete against the fatter, more flavorful, French-style product from older animals once consumers had tasted it and had a choice.

Bison grazier, Wayne Cobb, in Auburn, Kansas has found that some people want their meat lean and others want it fat. He agrees with his customers.

"I have two distinct markets for meat," he said. "I have a very lean meat market, which are customers sent to me by local heart doctors still on the lean meat kick. And I have followers of Sally Fallon and Doctor Adkins who are not afraid of fat and actually seek it out."

To serve these two markets he harvests the bulls as lean meat yearlings and the heifers as fat two-year-olds. All of the bison are field harvested with a rifle.

He said there is a Weston A. Price chapter in Topeka and they had been a wonderful customer for not only meat but also the bones for making broth. He sells his bison bones for $1.00 a pound. "That's another $150 a head," he said.

Agri-tainment

L eianneWright put on her best Star Trek voice and said "We are now going where no humans ever go—only cows. We are going into the pasture!"

With appropriate giggles, Leinanne's farm tour group of 65 kindergarten kids and first graders and their teachers marched single file up the steps of the large hay-filled wagon. This was the first of five school groups the Wright family would tour on the day I visited.

FARM TOURS are the latest enterprise for this innovative direct marketing oriented grass-based dairy farm. They also direct market whole milk, butter-

> *Sales on tour days at the Wright Dairy are typically 30 percent over a normal non-tour day.*

milk, cheese, ice cream, free-range eggs and a host of other farmstead produced items from an on-farm retail store. (All items sold are farmstead produced but not necessarily on the Wright farm.) I followed the kids up the retractable steps of the wagon to hear Leianne's pasture spiel. She used a bullhorn that can play "Old MacDonald's Farm" and was dressed in a long denim skirt and large brimmed straw hat. "This is show business. You have to look the part," she said.

157

I thought she did a wonderful job of presenting electric fences and the importance of grazing in producing quality milk in a first grade context. At one stop on the pasture tour, the cows all lined up by the fence for inspection like trained dogs and the children crowded to one side of the wagon for a closer look.

WANDA THE WONDER COW. After the pasture tour, the children filed off the hay wagon and into the rear of the dairy's old milking parlor which has been converted into a combination creamery-retail store. Here David Wright showed them his collection of antique dairy machinery including a 1947 Divco dairy delivery truck, a cream separator, hand churns, milk cans and glass milk bottles.

> *David sneaks in an advertisement by telling the kids they are always welcome to see the baby calves when their Mothers come to the farm to buy milk.*

Leianne's two blonde mules and the kids kept an eye on each other as they left the museum area and walked past their stalls.

The children then were allowed to hold some baby chicks, pet a small dairy goat and some ducks. They then filed into a small auditorium to watch the milking of "Wanda—the wonder cow."

David asked the kids to guess how much milk a cow made a day. He then had them count as he lined up the average day's milk production in one gallon plastic bottles. The kids were properly impressed. He then milked a small amount of milk from Wanda and put it into a calf-feeding bottle. "Now, let's go feed the calves," David said.

At the next-door calf feeding shed, the kids got to pet the new-born calves as they suckled the bottle of milk.

After the baby calves, the children filed back to where the tour started for a thorough hand-washing and free samples of Wright's Cane Break Farms whole milk and chocolate flavored whole milk.

Depending upon the time left before they have to return to school, the kids are free to try their hand at navigating a maze built of large hay roundbales. The maze is named the A-Maze-In-Hay.

LOGISTICS PLANNING. The tour times are staggered so that one group of children are on the pasture tour while another is touring the museum and milking demonstration. The tour reservations are bunched so that 300 or more children make the tour between nine and noon. The tour takes about 45 minutes to complete and costs $5 per head, adult or child.

Directing all of this logistical precision is David's sister, Susan Wright Manning, a recently retired school teacher and now full-time school tour director. "People ask me how I like being retired and I tell them I haven't had time to experience it yet," she said.

Susan said school teaching was good training for her new job because it was about dealing with people and that's what the tour business is about.

VIRTUOUS CIRCLE. The school tour business was almost completely developed through word-of-mouth. A small brochure of the farm's desire to have tours for school children was given to their milk customers who then found the school tour customers for them. In marketing terms, such a process of customers creating new customers for you is called a "virtuous circle."

HOLONIC FARM DIVISIONS. The Wright Dairy is being developed in a "holonic" fashion whereby each of the farm's revenue centers is made into a semi-freestanding business under one family member's supervision. School tours are Susan's "holon."

David's father grows out the dairy's replacements and grazes the dry cows on his own separate farm in another "holon."

Leianne has her own crabapple jelly "holon."

In a holonic business development, each holon is operationally independent but subservient to the long-term vision of senior management. In other words, the holons have to reinforce and strengthen the "whole" or centerpiece enterprise. (To learn more about this method of farm development, read my book *Knowledge Rich Ranching*.)

> *Learn to charge admission to your farm. Stop giving away high-value experiences in order to sell low-value agricultural products. In a paradigm switch, regard your grassfed meat, milk, eggs and chicken merely as the tools to enhance your real product, the experience of visiting a farm or ranch.*
>
> *Alice Valenzuela*

TOURS SELL MILK. "School tours are a profit center in and of themselves," David explained, "but they also help us in our larger goal which is to sell milk."

David said they quickly learned that children were the biggest fans of the taste of the farm's high butterfat, non-homogenized milk. The milk is pasteurized with hot water rather than steam to avoid the "cooked" flavor common to pasteurized milk.

"We've got a generation of Mothers who have never tasted real milk and aren't used to anything but the taste of skim or two percent (fat) milk. We've actually had cases where Mothers would pour store-bought commodity milk into our bottles to try and fool their children. However, the kids weren't fooled. They want the taste of real milk."

ENTERTAINING EDUCATION. Leianne said that while she had to entertain the kids on her pasture tour she was often subtly talking over the heads of the kids to the parents and teachers about the difference in pasture produced milk and the rest. She said the best tour groups for increasing milk sales were home-schooled kids because they had a large percentage of parents with them. A good tour day with one third of the tour party being adults can boost that day's retail milk sales by 30 to 40 percent.

Recently, the farm began offering occasional farm tours for customers and their children and grandchildren on Fridays and Saturdays. Many of the teachers on the school tours have come back and brought their own children for these tours. The family day tours have been tremendously successful so far in both tour income and increased milk sales but are worrisome because there is no guaranteed customer count as there is with a school tour.

"You need a minimum of 400 to 500 people to make a tour period worthwhile," David said. He said they typically schedule school farm tours for two mid-week days with 250 to 300 kids on each day. Most tour groups come from within a 50 to 60 mile radius of the farm but some have come from as far away as 120 miles. The Wright farm is in a rural area but is located on a very busy four-lane highway.

BIG WAGON IS ESSENTIAL. David first became interested in school tours from his cousin, Frank Randall, who has run school tours

> *The tours developed from handing a small brochure to all milk customers.*

of his sheep ranch near Auburn, Alabama for several years.

The other big inspiration was visiting Cagle Dairy near Atlanta who has made a large business out of school tours with some 700 to 800 students a day. He said the Cagles were very helpful and gave him some great ideas and advice.

"One of the things you absolutely must have is a tour wagon large enough to hold a bus load of kids," David said. Their home-made, 10 X 40 foot twelve-wheeled trailer can comfortably seat 60 to 65 children (which is the normal bus load) or 50 to 55 if half the load is adults. Small square bales placed back to back in the center of the trailer are the seating. The wagon is roofed and rain has not been a problem in conducting the tours.

School touring is labor intensive. It requires a minimum of six people to conduct a tour for a large group of students. David and Leianne said they are lucky they have family members, farm staff and neighbors who are willing to pitch in on tour days. However, they said you have to be careful to not push family loyalty and neighborliness too far.

> *Brian and Martha Goodsell of Candor, New York have found that agri-tourism fits well with their grassfed venison program. Currently the farm offers hunting, canoeing, tubing, hiking, cross country ski trails, local ATV and snowmobile trails, bicycle rentals, bird watching, wildlife tracking, tree, plant and wildflower study, fossil hunting, picknicking, group hay rides, a horseshoe pit, and a campfire pit. The Goodsells plan to add a B&B to give an "alternative" farm experience.*

"We plan to concentrate our school tours in the spring and fall when the weather is the nicest and the public schools are in session. The beautiful thing about school tours is that every year you've got a new crop of first graders to market to," David said.

YOUNG AND OLD CUSTOMERS . David Wright believes that if you are going to sell a perishable product like fresh milk you need to have a store so you can sell at the full retail price and equally important, so the customer can come to you rather than you having to go to her.

David said a big part of his business plan when he was planning to add direct marketing was to stay out of the transportation business. In researching other direct marketed dairies one of their biggest problems was high transportation costs.

Personally he would like to produce premium-priced organic milk but that would require him to ship it to Atlanta or Birmingham to sell it and put him in the transportation business. Living in culturally conservative rural Alabama, he decided he needed be conservative with both his pricing and his product posi-tioning.

"We tend to target the two extremes of the age spectrum in our milk marketing,"

Rose and Larry Mason of Dixon, Nebraska sell the majority of their grassfed bison meat to tourists who are attracted to their farm tour. Despite being a long way from anywhere, the ranch attracts some 6,000 visitors a year. The Masons charge $5.00 for a covered wagon tour of the 450-acre ranch.

After the tour, they offer the tour-ists a bison meat sandwich for $4.00.

"The key to our program is to get them to buy that sandwich. People won't buy what they haven't tried," Larry Mason said.

The Masons sell 85 percent of their meat during the May to September tourist season. Their big seller is buffalo summer sausage but they also sell buffalo jerky, steaks, roasts and bratwurst.

David said. "We do extremely well with kids and with retired people. For whatever reason, we do not do as well with people nearer our own age."

He first became interested in direct marketing because so many of his elderly neighbors were continually badgering him to sell them "real" milk. He said older people remember what farm fresh milk tasted like and were very dissatisfied with the local supermarket milk.

> *You can buy milk here on Tuesday and Friday (processing days) that is only four hours old. That's farm fresh.*

"We're lucky to be located in Alabama because supermarket milk here is both expensive and of very low quality." He said that 75 percent of the state's fluid milk is shipped in from West Texas or New Mexico. This often means supermarket milk is at least four days old by the time it gets to the store. "You can buy milk here on Tuesday and Friday (processing days) that is only four hours old," he said. "That's what I mean by farm fresh."

David goes to great care to keep his milk's taste as close to that of unpasteurized milk by using hot water for pasteurization rather than steam. He tastes each batch to make sure it doesn't have the cooked taste so common to supermarket milk. The milk is sold unhomogenized as many of his customers like to make their own butter.

He prices his milk below the brand-name milk but above the supermarket private label milk at $3.00 a gallon. He also sells buttermilk for $3.00 a gallon which is considerably under the supermarket price. In 2001 the farm sold 500 gallons of whole milk and 500 gallons of buttermilk a week.

He described the farm's buttermilk as being

164

made in the old-fashioned way and full of flavor. Among his elderly customers it is his biggest draw.

He added a two percent fat skimmed milk as many women would not drink a high fat, unhomogenized milk. While he had resisted selling it for personal health philosophy reasons, he said skimmed milk is actually more profitable for the farm because the skimmed cream can then be used for high profit ice cream.

His farmstead, high butterfat, premium ice cream is priced just under Blue Belle Ice Cream–a premium brand in the South–at $5.00 a half gallon. In 2001 the farm sold 150 to 180 gallons of its ice cream a week with a profit margin of approximately $3.00/half gallon.

If he ever decides to expand into the wholesale trade, he would do it with ice cream rather than fluid milk. "Ice cream meets the criteria of being both storable and portable and it doesn't go out of date like fluid milk does."

The "Amish" cheese and butter he sells is also priced considerably under supermarket cheese and initially brought in more gross sales dollars than his fluid milk sales.

> *Jan Moseley, a bison grazier and direct marketer near Dallas, encourages school tours of her ranch primarily because she wants access to the teachers. She has found school teachers to be an excellent market.*
>
> *"You're looking for an educated consumer," she said.*

"We try to fit in with everyday prices, " David said. "We require our customers to drive all the way out here to the farm to buy our product, so we need to give them some incentive."

165

ANOTHER AMAZING IDEA

Want to make some real money on a few acres of corn? Consider a corn maze.

Brett "Corn Maze" Herbst is the man to talk to. He is considered the guru of corn mazes. Starting with his first maze in 1996 in tiny American Fork, Utah, he has since designed 205 mazes across the United States and Canada. His company, Maize LLC, currently has over 100 maze sites under five-year contracts for annual design and installation.

Herbst said his father thought he was insane when he quit his job to build his first maze.

"I grossed $63,000 in six weeks. After that my father never criticized my decision to quit my job again."

Herbst said most mazes are three to six acres in size. The largest corn maze ever built in the world (which he designed) was 12 acres.

Some of his maze clients gross over $200,000 in a few weeks and most net between $30,000 and $50,000 during their six week runs. However, some have lost money.

He said some people just don't get "show business" and its demands to be personable and welcoming. Other than operator personality, he said a corn maze is a game of "location, location, location."

> *A good maze operator is someone who is well-organized, a people person and who can talk to the media with enthusiasm.*

The best location is near an Interstate highway exit or near a well-known local landmark that can be given with directions. "Fifteen miles on a road you travel everyday is a lot shorter than 15 miles on road you have never been on," he said.

Herbst is a partner in three mazes in Utah and owns one outright. These mazes have attracted 650,000 visitors over the last four years.

His personal maze is located 40 miles north of Salt Lake City near an Interstate exit. In 2001, this maze attracted 25,000 regular visitors and 3,000 school kids on

Maze locations can be quite remote as long as they are on frequently traveled roads.

tour. The maze is priced at six dollars for adults, $3.50 for four to 11 year olds, and free for those under four. The haunted barnyard and hayride are nine dollars. The cow train is a dollar. Field trips for school kids go for two dollars for the maze. The wagon ride is three dollars and the train ride is free.

Due to E coli concerns, the petting zoo can only be viewed by small children from the train.

FALL HARVEST SEASON IS BEST

The fall "harvest season" is the best time for a maze. "No one wants to go into a corn field when it is hot," he said. In Utah, Labor Day weekend is a good time to open. The season ends at Halloween.

His personal maze includes a hay ride to a "haunted barnyard," a kiddie train ride and a petting zoo. The hayride goes through a tunnel made of black plastic draped over a hogwire frame. Rubber snakes dangle from its ceiling.

Labor is the biggest cost of a maze. At the seasonal peak before Halloween, Herbst's maze employs 30 employees as ticket takers, popcorn sellers, "spooks" and "corn cops." These employees are mostly retired people and college students.

The corn cops ensure order and give a helping

hand to those hopelessly lost in the maze. The spooks are there to surprise visitors on their journey through the corn maze.

The maze opens in the late afternoon and continues until early evening. The maze is not lighted. Visitors are encouraged to bring flashlights after dark. After dark visitors are mostly high school and college students who like being scared.

> *Corn cops ensure order and give a helping hand to those hopelessly lost in the maze.*

A new attraction at his maze was a giant pumpkin slingshot. In 2001 a large cartoon of Usama Bin Laden was provided as a target and pumpkins were sold as ammunition for a dollar a piece.

He sold $10,000 worth of home-grown pumpkins with the attraction and plans to expand his farm's pumpkin acreage.

DESIGN IS KEY TO MEDIA ATTENTION

Herbst said the design of the maze is critical because it is how you attract media attention and make your attraction unique. "No one is going to pay money to just walk through a corn field."

Good designs are religious symbols, patriotic motifs, star navigation charts and designs that tie in with local events. For example, his personal maze in 2001 celebrated the 2002 Winter Olympics in Salt Lake City.

> *Media coverage and marketing are the key to a successful maze.*

None of Herbst's maze designs have dead ends. All designs lead the customer in a circular fashion which helps with crowd flow.

The corn field is planted solid in corn and then

the design is sprayed into the corn with a herbicide. He has an organic herbicide made from citric acid that works well and which some clients insist upon.

Mazes no-tilled into pastures are best because they are less muddy. He said in a tilled field the maze must be closed if it rains due to excessive mud. He said irrigation is absolutely essential because the corn is normally planted during the driest part of the summer. The design is sprayed on when the corn is one to two feet tall. Sunflowers and flowers are then planted to add color.

Herbst has two teams that travel the country in late summer spraying in Herbst's maze designs. He currently has 104 clients under contract for design and installation. Herbst receives an annual fee plus six percent of the maze's gross.

Once the corn is well up and still green, a plane is hired to fly over and take a picture of the design. This picture then becomes the focal point of the maze's publicity campaign.

"Media coverage and marketing are the key to a successful maze," he said. "A quality press kit is a huge factor. The best maze in the world is no good if no one knows about it."

He provides his clients with a manual on marketing and operations. This kit includes sample radio spots.

A good maze design should take the average person an hour to navigate.

Typically the first two to three years are an educational process for the operator. However, the crowds grow each year. He said good crowds attract even bigger crowds. "People like to be around people having fun. No one comes alone to a maze. People always go with family and friends."

He said it was critical that the maze design change every year as this was what made a long-running maze news. He admitted that free media coverage becomes more difficult for long-running mazes and that they must rely more on paid advertising. He said some high-traffic sites spend as much as $60,000 a year on advertising.

Herbst said many of his clients were direct-marketing-oriented farmers who used the corn maze to attract people to their farm. They hope some of them will become long-term customers.

He said he thought mazes on real working farms were more attractive to customers.

And what does he do with the standing corn after Halloween?

He grazes it off with cattle.

Spreading the Word

I read an interesting book called **The Tipping Point** by Malcolm Gladwell that should be of particular interest to producers of grassfed meat and dairy products. This book is primarily interested in the how and why some products and practices become "cool." Coolness cannot be purchased with advertising. It must come from word-of-mouth marketing. He calls these word-of-mouth marketing phenomenons "social epidemics."

Gladwell said that all social epidemics start with a very select group of people. He has divided this small group which he calls "The Select Few" into three segments, which he labels as connectors, mavens and salesmen.

* CONNECTORS are people who know lots of people. These are the quintessential people persons. They are the party givers. The people who collect social relationships the way some people collect stamps. They know someone who knows someone who can get done what you need done.

Quite often these people are politically connected as well. Every community has one or two of these people.

Give them a sample of your product. Cultivate their friendship.

171

* MAVENS are the second segment of people. Mavens are people who accumulate knowledge. While the vast majority of people aren't really paying attention to what is going on around them, mavens are.

A maven knows an awful lot about a small area of expertise and so we tend to rely on them for sorting out truthful information from the con artists. These are the people who keep the marketplace honest.

For example, in the realm of grassfed-related health and nutrition, Jo Robinson is a maven. In international dairying thought, Irish dairy grazier Michael Murphy is a maven.

However, a maven is not a persuader. A maven is a source of information whose sole motivation is to educate and to help. They are the teachers. To make something happen requires the final segment which Gladwell calls salesmen.

* SALESMEN have the skill to persuade us when we are unconvinced of what we are hearing. The essence of a Salesman is that on some level, they cannot be resisted. This is called charisma. It is the ability to infect other people with the emotions the salesman himself is feeling.

The Sequence of Events for a Successful Grassfed Product:

1. Get the production information you need.
2. Produce it for your own family.
3. Give some to your friends.
4. Sell it to your friends' friends who ask for it.
5. Make it a business.

What makes a good salesman is the ability to project the feeling that he cares as much or more about you and your well-being as he does himself. Joel Salatin is an excellent example of a salesman.

According to Gladwell, "If you are interested in starting a word-of-mouth epidemic, your resources ought to be solely concentrated on those three groups. No one else matters."

Of course, these three groups of people must also have what Gladwell calls a "sticky" story to tell. The average American is now exposed to 254 different commercial messages every day–most of which bounce off of us with as little effect as rain on a tin roof.

Gladwell said we only listen to those messages which can be made practical and personal to us.

For example, men pay no more attention to advertisements for women's personal products than women pay to ads for men's aftershave.

Human beings can only handle so much information at once. To prevent information overload we filter out all extraneous information not directed specifically at what we are interested in learning more about.

In family situations, we tend to fight information

MAVENS are the data banks. They provide the message.

CONNECTORS are the social glue. They spread the message around.

The SALESMAN's charisma allows us to suspend our natural disbelief of anything new.

overload by assigning responsibility for certain messages to certain family members. For example, if you have a son who is a computer enthusiast you will probably assign him the responsibility for paying attention to and remembering stuff dealing with computers. Why should you clutter up your brain learning how to load software on a com-

> *Assign new farm enterprises to one of your children rather than take it on yourself.*

puter when you have a son handy who already knows how to do this? Why should a man have to remember where he put his truck keys when he has a wife who can remember for him?

Since mental energy is limited, we concentrate on what we do best and defer to our home-raised experts on subjects outside our assigned interest responsibility. This makes everyone in the family more mentally efficient.

When a person asks that you talk to their spouse about the subject you are trying to sell them, it means the subject is in the other spouse's interest of responsibility. Men tend to concentrate on family financial issues and those things that are dirty, smelly, have a motor attached to them, are dead or are needing to be killed

> *New products and ideas frequently move faster with women because they tend to be more networked into groups than men.*

(like spiders and snakes). In contrast, it is typically women who become their family's "expert" in health and nutrition.

Herein lies the great conundrum of farmer-to-consumer direct marketing. We typically have a man trying to sell new health and nutrition ideas to a woman. I have had some personal experience with this and it is really tough. The best thing you can do is to give her some literature and let her sell herself.

I've read over 100 farmer-to-consumer grassfed product brochures and it is obvious that most were written by men. They are invariably about things (the ranch, the cows, the grass) rather than about emotions (healthy children, a husband who doesn't fall over dead tomorrow from a heart attack, happy contented animals). Such emotional writing doesn't come naturally to most men. That's why we shouldn't try to do it.

I have long believed that in the farm triad of production, marketing and finance, marketing communications should be in the wife's interest of responsibility. This is true in commodity farming but is doubly true in direct-to-consumer food marketing. If you can't talk your wife into accepting this responsibility then find a woman somewhere who will.

> # *Radio Church Services*
>
> *David Wright of Alexandria, Alabama has found that sponsoring Sunday morning church services on a local radio station is a good way to attract the elderly people who are customers for his farm's buttermilk. He has found that running ads every other week draws as well as running every week.*

Similarly, don't waste too much time trying to proselytize your town's male doctors. Doctors live in a world of tightly regulated peer approval. They do not (and cannot) take kindly to new ideas from the laity.

A much better use of your time and money might be to give Jo Robinson's book *Why Grassfed is*

Best! to the nurses. The doctor sees the patient a few minutes a day. The nurse is there for an eight hour shift, really gets to know the patient and knows firsthand the pain and suffering cancer and heart disease causes. Nurses can be very effective allies. Recruit them. Invite them over for an Argentine style asado barbecue.

Malcolm Gladwell observed that if you want to get a woman's undivided attention for a couple of hours, sell her hairdresser on your product. Now, this is difficult for men to understand but apparently women have an incredibly trusting relationship with their hairdressers. They literally let their hair down there.

Hairdressers are excellent connectors. They communicate easily and well with others, have a wide variety of acquaintances and tend to be very intuitive. So, give your wife's hairdresser a great free steak and a copy of Jo's book.

CALIFORNIA HERE WE COME

Whether it is the garden club, or Bible study, women spend a lot more time together sharing thoughts and ideas. According to Gladwell, the most networked group of women in the USA is in the San Francisco area. If you want a female-oriented idea to catch fire in America, this is where the kindling is.

My wife Carolyn and I just happen to know two very networked women in Marin County across the Bay from San Francisco. Pat is married to a pro-environment, retired elected official (Republican) and Beth is married to the

> *The term organic creates an impression of knowledge without really conveying information.*

owner of a national chain of personal-growth seminar companies.

We knew both were heavy into organic foods and alternative nutrition, so we mailed them a copy of Jo Robinson's book and then flew out for a visit a few weeks later. It is Jo Robinson's belief that organic food consumers will be the easiest to convert to grassfed products and we thought this would be a good test of her hypothesis.

> *Everybody assumes they know what organic means.*

We found Jo was correct. Both were very agitated when we arrived. They said they had no idea that all organic meat and milk **wasn't** grassfed. The first thing they wanted to do was for us to go to their local organic supermarket and locate some healthy grassfed food products.

I taught them to read the fine print (very fine print) on the labels. They were even more shocked to find that most "range chickens" were just raised in a conventional chicken house with an open door to an exercise yard. It said so right on the label.

An egg label touted that its chickens were fed an "all vegetarian diet." Surely that means pasture-raised, they said. Nope, a "vegetarian diet" label said it was soybean meal and grain.

Pat took us to a small non-chain organic grocery where she was sure we'd find REAL food. I read the label of a sprouted grain bread, that was a popular favorite of Pat's. "Where do you think this comes from?" I asked. She said she thought it came from a small country bakery somewhere in Napa. "Nope, New Jersey." The label also clearly said the organic tomatoes were from Mexico. So, much for supporting local farmers.

"Raised on natural hay and grain in the fresh air of an open lot," is how one large organic dairy described their production technique on the side of its container. In other words, nothing different from the conventional California confinement mega-dairy but at double the retail price.

One dairy's brochure talked in length about a specific dairy they bought their milk from where the cows were grazed. However in an E-mail inquiry they admitted only about half of their milk came from grass. Of course, their label had a cartoon cow with a clover plant hanging out of its mouth.

At Whole Foods, I approached the meat manager and asked him if his beef was grassfed.

"Yes, sir. We serve only Oregon Country Beef here," he said.

I told him I didn't think Oregon Country was a grassfed product. He insisted it was. To prove his point, he went and got their brochure. "See it says they are committed to a set of 'graze well' principles. That means its grassfed beef."

I looked at the small brochure. It talked glowingly of cowboys and blue skies and green grass right up to the one sentence near the end where it said that cattle ownership is retained through the feedlot.

> *The primary way we can sell people on a new food product is by allowing them to sample it. The more different it is from the commonplace, the higher the price we can charge for it.*

I pointed this sentence out to the meat manager. He just shook his head in disbelief. "They sure don't make that very obvious do they?" No, they don't. And as a producer, that's why you should.

Pat and Beth were particularly dismayed to read that the salmon they had been buying was farm raised.

"We hardly ever get any real fish from the ocean anymore," the fish market manager at a Wild Oats supermarket told us. So much for salmon as a good source of Omega-3.

Most organic consumers aren't getting what they think they are buying. This is what Joel Salatin has been saying for years. Here's what he told his customers in one of his customer newsletters:

> *The best source verification for consumers is to buy their food directly from a farm.*
> **Joel Salatin**

"The term organic creates an impression of knowledge, without really conveying information. Actual (production) techniques, obviously, can be as different as good and bad, but using the term organic eliminates information-based conversation because everyone assumes they know what organic means."

This is exactly what we found with our friends in California. They assumed that organic beef meant grassfed, that an organic salmon had been feeding on green plankton in the ocean and that the vegetables and bread came from farms and businesses that were both small and local. Once they found this not to be true they were terribly disillusioned.

"Why should we pay twice as much for food that isn't that different from the regular supermarket?" one asked.

Therein lies a trap for the whole organic movement. Market research has shown that consumers who buy an organic or natural product are buying into a "whole." In the consumer's mind this whole revolves around things that are small in scale, local in origin and is produced as close to the way Nature does it as possible.

If a product that is labeled organic or natural is

179

found out to not be any of these, the consumer feels conned. This is why many believe there must be something "beyond organic" that would also "source verify" and specify the production techniques used as well.

> *Pass-fail systems never encourage excellence. They encourage minimalism.*
>
> *Joel Salatin*

Joel Salatin said the best source verification is for consumers to buy their food directly from a farm. He believes that you cannot write a standard tight enough that unscrupulous producers can't fudge on it.

"Standards are only as good as the integrity of the producer/processor and the premium organic market is attracting more and more unprincipled individuals hoping to cash in on the clean food movement," Joel said.

The ultimate result of our San Francisco shopping trip was that the only ruminant product we could find in any of the "health food" stores we visited that would remotely be high in Omega 3 and CLA was imported New Zealand lamb. And of course, that's what our friends bought. (No American lamb—grass or grainfed—was for sale in the any of the organic supermarkets we visited.)

While we were in California we went through the Napa wine-producing region. Every small winery had a sign on the highway advertising "free tastings." The reason for this is that wine varies in taste due to the skill of the vinter. Due to the rapid growth of the California wine industry, there is an awful lot of really bad wine being produced.

We can spend a hundred years arguing the intellectual pros and cons of grassfeeding or like the

Napa vinters you can let them try your product and settle it in a few seconds.

If your product tastes good and is tender and also happens to help fight cancer and heart disease, you've probably got a customer and a potential evangelist for the cause.

HEALTH BENEFITS OF GRASSFED PRODUCTS

Doctor Tilak Dhiman of Utah State University is one of North America's leading researchers on the relationship between CLA in meat and milk and human health. Speaking at the University of Nebraska's conference on "The Future of Grassfed Meats and Milk," Dr. Dhiman said that he was now convinced that grassfed food products were "not only preventative but regenerative as well."

By this he meant that grassfed foods could not just prevent health problems but could help people who already have chronic health problems get better.

He said current research with animals indicates that CLA (conjugated linoleic acid, which is found in the fat of grassfed ruminants) not only reduces the incidence of cancer in animals but that it also suppresses the growth of cancer cells.

He said that definitive human studies would take many more years. Until then the health benefits of grassfed foods would have to be legally stated as "potential health benefits."

Currently, animal studies suggest that CLA is:
1. Anti-carcinogenic
2. Reduces body fat
3. Anti-diabetic
4. Anti-antherosclerosis (heart disease)

Dr. Dhiman said to keep in mind that CLA was additive. In other words, eating grassfed meat, cheese

181

and milk all helped to accumulate CLA in body tissues.

A French study of 360 women found that the higher the CLA level was in their breast tissue the lower their incidence of breast cancer was.

He said the minimum effective level of CLA was .5 percent of the total diet. While this was a tiny amount, this was almost impossible to achieve eating normal American supermarket foods.

However, he said grassfed foods are so high in CLA that a single eight ounce glass of grassfed milk, plus one 30 gram (one ounce) slice of cheese from grassfed milk and one 84 gram (2.5 ounces) serving of grassfed meat provided twice the minimum amount of CLA needed for both prevention and regeneration.

Dhiman said that 100 percent grassfed meats and milk were up to 500 percent higher in CLA than meat and milk fed conventional high-grain diets. The key element here is "100 percent grassfed."

Currently the USA has the least amount of CLA in its diet of any country in the world. However, this is a relatively recent phenomenon. As recently as 1947, seventy percent of all beef eaten in the USA was grassfed.

Unfortunately, a lot of graziers think a little grain won't hurt, but it does. For example, the milk from dairy cows fed as little as 15 pounds of grain per day is not significantly higher in CLA than that of a conventional confinement dairy. He said it was not a question of how few pounds of grain a day a dairyman could feed. He said the benchmark for high CLA milk had to be "no grain."

He said that dairy cows turning out to pasture and fed no grain produced the peak amount of CLA in their milk after just five days of grazing.

In contrast, Dhiman said beef steers that had been fed a small amount of grain during their winter backgrounding period and then finished on pasture with no grain had half the CLA in their meat of steers backgrounded on hay alone and finished on pasture.

He said that dairy cows fed only hay produced 60 percent of the CLA of cows grazing fresh pasture.

> *The benchmark for achieving high levels of CLA is feeding no grain.*

However, the milk from the hay-only cows was twice as high as that from cows fed a typical hay-plus-grain diet.

"It's okay if you have to feed some hay," he said. "Just stay away from grain."

Dhmian said length of cut in hay and silage was an important factor in CLA production as well. For maximum CLA production the length of cut should closely approximate that from grazing (four to six inches).

Grinding hay tremendously lowers its CLA production potential.

He said that pasture silage was better than hay and the less the silage wilted the better it was for CLA production.

Dhiman said that a pasture sward that maximized animal gain or milk production would also maximize CLA production.

For example, he said that a ranch in Oregon whose well-finished meat impressed a *New York Times* food section editor as the best steak she had ever eaten also had the highest CLA percentage of any meat he had tested.

"It's a win-win game. High CLA and good eating quality go together," he said.

183

MORE BENEFITS OF GRASSFED FOODS

In addition to CLA, Dhiman said that grassfed foods also had the following:

300 percent more Vitamin E

75 percent more Omega-3

78 percent more Beta-carotene

400 percent more Vitamin A

Grassfed beef is not only much lower in fat and higher in protein than grainfed beef but it is much safer to eat due to the relative absence of E-coli.

VITAMIN E

Dhiman said that Vitamin E is a potent anti-oxidant that lowers the risk of both heart disease and cancer. Anti-oxidants are also considered to be "anti-aging" agents that help your body resist the negative impacts of oxidation.

He said Vitamin E deficiency is diet related and that grassfed beef has 300 percent more Vitamin E than grainfed beef.

OMEGA-3

He said that grassfed meats have 75 percent more Omega-3 fatty acids than grainfed beef.

Omega-3 is a potent anti-cancer agent and is essential for a sharp, well functioning brain. It also reduces blood pressure and lowers heart attack risk.

For good health a 2-to-1 Omega-6 to Omega-3 ratio is recommended. The diet of most Americans is currently estimated to be 20-to-1.

VITAMIN A

Dhiman said that Vitamin A was also a cancer fighter and is linked to both good vision and good sex. It is also necessary for good bone development and the

184

prevention of skin disorders.

He said that human health was a combination of food, environment, lifestyle and genetics. He said that the promotion of vegetarianism as a more healthy lifestyle was not born out by health statisitics. People who eat both meat and vegetables have 72 percent less colon cancer than those who only eat vegetables.

He feels that healthy foods should be both organic and grass based. He said he felt there were definite potential health risks from pesticides, chemicals, hormones and GMOs.

He said that in our rush to promote new health findings like CLA we should not lose sight that Nature's way of producing it would always be the best.

He said that CLA could be artificially raised slightly higher than that found on pasture through the feeding of large amounts of sunflower oil to feedlot cattle. However, this would not increase any of the other naturally occurring grassfed benefits.

Additional Research

Research at Cornell University found four common food spices to be 100 percent effective against every bacterial species tested. These four were onion, garlic, allspice and oregano.

Chili peppers, cinnamon, cumin, lemongrass, bay leaf, and cloves were found to reduce the growth of bacteria by 70 percent.

Another major anti-bacterial agent widely used in cooking is salt.

OTHER VALUES

He said that grassfed foods have a whole bundle of benefits of which CLA is only one benefit. Some of the parts of this bundle are:

They are cheaper to produce.

They are nutritious.

They are environmentally safe to produce.

They produce a prettier landscape.

They produce naturally healthy animals.

And, they lend themselves well to organic production.

STRONGER FLAVOR

Dr. Dhiman also said that research has shown grassfed beef also has twice the flavor of grainfed beef.

While this may be a problem with some consumers who prefer the bland, veal-like minimal flavor of grainfed beef, he believed that in the long-run a full-flavored beef would be preferred.

"We must be very cognizant of the fact that the grasses we feed and the stress we put on our animals will be reflected in the flavor of the meat. We desperately need research into the flavoring effect the various grasses have."

> *Your best health will result from your eating as close to nature as possible. We are creatures of nature, not of lab science.*
>
> ***Dr. Tilak Dhiman***

He said it is critical that American graziers learn how to finish their cattle. He said the current widespread practice of killing animals before they are fully finished results in beef that has minimal flavor, is difficult to cook without toughening and is difficult for the consumer to swallow due to the lack of fat.

ADVERTISING

Anecdotal evidence suggests that classified advertising does not work well with premium-priced food products. You can be small but your ads had better look as clean and professional as the big guys.

Small and frequent newspaper display ads seem to be most cost-effective with niche food products in small towns. In large cities where newspaper ad rates are out of reach of small businesses, look for cheaper, more targeted media such as community newspapers and alternative newspapers.

> *If you stop advertising, the average person will assume that you have gone out of business.*

If you are attractive and articulate, you may find television ads on your local cable company to be cost-effective. Just keep in mind that the potential customer expects your television ad to look just as professional as the established brands. This "look" is extremely expensive to produce.

A truism of advertising is that once you start it, you can never stop it. A major role of advertising is to reassure the consumer that you are still there and still want his business.

What absolutely does not work is advertising an undifferentiated commodity. "Eat more beef" we advertise. This is similar to an ad urging people to "Breathe more air." People can't eat what isn't there. They currently eat all we produce.

If we want them to eat more, we just have to produce more.

What we really want is not higher consumption but a higher price. A higher price only comes from market differentiation.

Our poultry competitors are not advertising

187

generic chicken. They are advertising their chicken and why it is different and special. The primary role of advertising is to say, "Here is a product we have designed just for you."

Who wants a product designed for everybody? Nobody.

The reason these commodity advertising programs are so popular are that they appear to offer hope without the individual producer having to do anything different. Hoping for an improvement in circumstance with no change in action on our part has been given as a definition for insanity.

SIGNS:

* For highway signs, the height of each letter should be in proportion to the traffic speed—one inch per ten mph.

*Red or black on white is easiest to read.

*Use keywords to quickly attract attention. Pasture-raised. Grass fed. Drug free.

*If local ordinances prohibit billboards, consider using portable signs.

*Turn your pick-up or panel truck into a moving billboard.

*If you have a logo or distinctive type style, keep it consistent with your letterhead, newsletter, shopping bags, order forms and signs.

PUBLIC RELATIONS

David and Kay Morrissey of Anderson, South Carolina, raise and direct market pastured poultry, grassfed beef and pastured lamb. They have the only Highland herd of cattle in the state and the shaggy animals are so unique that they are in demand as displays in area fairs and parades. The Morrisseys also provide cattle and sheep for church Christmas pageants.

Dave compares teaching someone about the way his farm operates to trying to convince someone visiting New York City for the first time to try a bagel. "Once they try it they will have a new standard to judge all other bagels by for the rest of their lives."

"People need to be educated that there is a better product out there and why it is better," said Dave. "The last few generations of Americans have lost their link to the family farm, so we continually invite people out to visit the operation. Parents and grandparents love to bring the kids out to the farm. Seeing a child hold a lamb, catch a live chicken, or pick up an egg is fun to behold and to think it might be the only farm they will ever visit is kind of sobering."

Whenever possible Dave accepts speaking engagements at local service clubs, women's clubs and schools. Potential customers are also encouraged to bring their children and grandchildren to the farm to see the animals. One year they received free and unexpected publicity when the Highlander escaped from the pen and had to be rounded up downtown.

"Never a dull moment," said Kay.

Create a news release about your product or market location and give it to your county extension office. They can distribute it to local and city newspapers.

SELLING TO RESTAURANTS:

* When selling to restaurants seek those who say they have a chef, not a cook. Chefs are food savvy and more likely to seek unique ingredients for their menus.

* Restaurants with changing menus offer greater opportunities for your seasonal meat and dairy products.

* Target restaurants commensurate in size to the amount of meat you can supply.

* Provide samples to allow the chef to make his own cooking comparisons.

SOME WILD IDEAS

"All buffalo are born equal but they aren't raised equal." This is a quote from Dave Hutchinson's ranch brochure and emphasizes his dis-satisfaction with the drift of some bison producers into what he considers to be "un-natural" production models—genetic tinkering to produce larger animals, hormonal additives, high fat content in the meat and grain finishing.

Hutchinson runs the 5000-acre Perfect 10 Buffalo Ranch at Rose, Nebraska and produces and sells grassfed bison meat. He thinks consumers want a totally natural grassfed bison meat. Perfect 10 Buffalo advertises that their "Buffalo graze on natural prairie grass and drink artesian well water." To add further marketing distinction, the 5000-acre ranch is certified as organic.

Hutchinson initially got interested in meat production because the ranch's buffalo breeding stock advertising attracted a lot of ranch visitors who all wanted to sample buffalo meat. The bison meat they bought commercially was so bad Hutchinson was embarrassed to serve it.

This spurred them to slaughter a few grassfed bulls for their own consumption and prove to themselves that bison meat could be a quality eating experience. Soon afterward a restaurant in Lincoln, Nebraska showed up at the ranch looking for a "gimmick" to boost its sales. The restaurant was across the street from a major heart disease hospital—a natural location for selling lean buffalo meat.

They took a live buffalo and built a temporary corral in the restaurant parking lot, which attracted free publicity for the restaurant and quickly turned its fortunes around. Success stories travel quickly. Soon other restaurants began to call for bison meat. Today, Cisco Foods handles Perfect 10's restaurant meat distribution in all states except Colorado where Dave's daughter, Channtel, handles the meat sales.

Chad Peterson said the only retail outlet in the tiny town near his Nebraska bison ranch was a Conoco service station. He offered to put two bison on an empty lot next to the service station as a draw to passing tourists.

In return, Chad asked the service station to sell his grassfed bison meat and give him 100 percent of the proceeds. The service station agreed. This provides Chad with $200 to $300 a week in sales.

"Our primary meat salesmen are chefs. The average tenure of a chef at a restaurant is three years. When they move they add our meat to the menu of their new restaurant."

191

The Perfect 10 Buffalo Ranch has a free ranch grass tour each summer open to anyone interested in grazing and grassfed meat production. This tour includes a free buffalo steak lunch.

NEWSLETTERS

"You can never open yourself up too much to your customers. Level with them," said Joel Salatin, speaking at a *Stockman Grass Farmer* "Grass finished Meat and Milk" conference. "Anytime someone gives you constructive criticism, acknowledge it. It shows you're listening."

In communicating with your customers through a newsletter, Joel offered these suggestions:

* Be personable.

* The more snazzy the design (also with a label and packaging), the more likely customers are to think you're cutting corners somewhere with your product.

"We have never sought media hype for our place," he said.

However, press releases can generate media attention. For example, a weather story (drought, extended periods of rain, etc.) might explain how your management system handles the situation. You might announce tours for school children or a new product. If it's different and distinctive enough, (the media attention) will happen by itself. The energy builds.

Brian Moyer, a Berks County, Pennsylvania farmer and direct marketer writes his newsletter as if he's talking to friends. "It's not just about what's for sale. It's trying to make them feel they are a part of the farm."

STAY IN TOUCH:

When selling meat seasonally, it's important to keep in touch with your customers during the off season.

* Tell your customers how much you appreciate them and hope they'll refer their friends to you.

* Let your customers know you plan to be in this for the long haul and you appreciate them growing with you.

* Create a customer appreciation Christmas card list.

* Send postcards at unexpected times of the year— reminders or thank yous for buying "clean and green, pasture-raised products" at St. Patrick's day.

* Mail an early-bird newsletter or notice in the slow winter months.

* Off season is an excellent time to include cooking tips, recipes, or educational information about the health benefits of grass-finished meats.

* Including self-addressed envelopes help speed order replies.

* For relationship marketing, create a card file on each customer with notes about spouses, children's names, pets, personal interests and such.

* Lagniappe, add "a little something extra" to large purchases—a spice jar of herbs for use with grassfed lamb or recipes. Be creative. Assemble packets of dry ingredients that might be used as a meat rub for roasts.

TALK ABOUT ME!

I feel that one of the most significant country music songs ever written—at least from a marketing standpoint - is the song "Talk about me!" by Toby Keith.

The gist of this song is that the singer is tired of you always talking about you and wants some time to "talk about me." Talk about my needs, my wants, not about you, you, you, he sings.

Most of the brochures I have read for Farm Fresh products could heed this singer's advice. They are not written about what the farm's products can do for the customer. Instead, they are about their farm, their cows, their kids, their needs and the great time they are having living in the country. While this is a great ego trip for the farm owner it won't sell much product.

Verne and Linda Hubalek of Lindsborg, Kansas sell one third of their bison meat over the Internet and ship filets, steaks, roasts and other products to customers as far away as New York and Maine.

They also sell through a local supermarket. The meat is sold in a variety of packages at prices ranging from $17.95 for four pounds of ground burger to $598.95 for a variety pack filled with 100 pounds of various cuts.

As the song says, your customer most wants you to "talk about me."

The things that are important to you about what you are doing need to be turned around and expressed in the context of what they do for the customer.

For example, if you want to run a picture of your children in the brochure, explain that because you have

194

children you know how concerned your customers are for the health and well-being of *their* children.

If you want to run a picture of your livestock, explain that they are managed so as to provide meat that is not only healthy but full-flavored and juicy.

And if you want to run a picture of yourself, you had better have a smile on your face and look healthy and wholesome as well.

The same holds true for Web sites.

INTERNET LINKS

The odds of a potential customer accidentally finding your Web site are pretty small. The best way to generate Internet business is to obtain a link to a high traffic site. In grassfed meats and dairy products, one of the best sites to link to is Jo Robison's eatwild.com. This is a news and information site for health issues concerning grassfed meats and milk products.

To obtain a link to this site go to the Suppliers' page and click on Request for Information. This will allow you to download an application form. If you meet the criteria, you can mail the signed application to the address given along with the fee to be included as a supplier.

Site operator, Jo Robinson, said she receives between 1000 and 1700 individual hits on a good day. Robinson keeps the site in the public eye with frequent speeches and media interviews.

UNTANGLING THE WEB

Richard Parry of Foxfire Farms in Ignacio, Colorado reports that his Web site cost $1000 for its original design, but he could hire it done for half that amount today. Later he sent two of his children to a local Web design school to learn how to modify and update the site. Most of his sales of grassfed lamb have been to Californians who regard Colorado as "clean and green."

Parry has found that to do any significant business on the Internet you need the ability to take credit cards. Since many people are still reluctant to give their credit card numbers to an Internet site, create an order form your customer can print out and mail in.

> *Lasater Grasslands Beef is sold through natural foods stores in Colorado and on the Internet. The ranch estimates that they get one order a day from the Internet.*

B to B Magazine recommends that you avoid bluster and exaggeration on your Web site. The magazine said exaggeration detracts from the credibility of your entire site and brand. If your claim is really outstanding your visitors will realize it by reading the supporting evidence. The number one reason people are using the Web is to get information, so the magazine recommends that you cut the fluff and say it simply and concisely without exaggeration.

WEB TIPS

One of the first things you need to ask is who is your audience? What do they want? This defines your goals for the site.

What are your goals? What do you want the site to accomplish? Sales? A mailing list? Links to other sites? A personal connection with your customers? If you don't know who your audience is you're designing the Web site for yourself.

Getting people to come to your site is a marketing challenge. Getting repeat visitors is a planning challenge.

196

Content dictates return visits. Without compelling content, the Web site becomes a brochure rather than a working Web site.

Regular updates encourage return visits.

People only give a Web page three seconds before deciding whether to stay and read more or leave.

Your job is to show the Web browser in what Seth Godin describes in *The Big Red Fez, How to Make Any Web Site Better* as an "obvious, obvious, obvious," way what you want them to do.

Prepare only one main objective per page.

For each objective you have to design a single page.

If your site asks for customer information (such as a name and address for you to collect in a database of potential customers, or a form to place an on-line order), do not use scroll-down buttons. This slows down the browser by forcing them to take their hands off the keyboard to use the mouse. Stick to what's simple.

If your site is set up to encourage customers to buy on-line, make it easy for them to complete the purchase. Have a

Jim and Ellie Krise of Terry, Montana have found the Internet to be a good way to sell the grassfed organic beef they produce on their remote ranch. In March of 2000, they went online with their Web site.

Ellie said it took about three months of spare time to build the ranch's Web site. Thanks to the Web site they have developed an on-line friendship with grassfed beef producers in France who discovered their Web site. Check it out at 4k-ranch.com.

button, list, or link to the purchase page on several pages.

Make your contact information–phone number, address–easy to find on one or more pages of the Web site.

Test the paths on your site regularly to be sure it is the working the way you intend.

"The most common place to click on any Web page is the top left-hand corner," advises Godin. Make it obvious. Use red.

Make it easy for the viewer to share comments with you.

"Once someone is online she's only a click away from your competition," Godin warns.

After a customer has bought something and the transaction is complete, follow up with a thank you page. You might offer them a free issue of your next newsletter, or offer to notify them by e-mail of your next seasonal sale or processing dates.

When customers are satisfied with your product, let *them* spread the word. Include a page that lets them send it to a friend, whose name, e-mail, address and comment they'll fill in.

Simplify, simplify, simplify.

Food related Web sites making health claims are subject to regulation by the Federal Trade Commission. The FTC said Web site health claims will be judged by the same standards that apply to all FTC-regulated products. All health claims must be accompanied by solid, competent, reliable scientific evidence to support the claim.

ANIMAL WELFARE

Jan Moseley, who raises and sells grassfed bison near Dallas, has found the primary thing her Internet customers are concerned about is the animal's welfare.

"We've found that consumers of specialty meats want a lot of information. They particularly want to know how the animals are raised. We emphasize that our animals have never been castrated, de-horned, injected with hormones or antibiotics, feedlotted or fed grain. New customers consistently comment that they are buying our meat because they like the way we are raising our animals," Jan said.

According to the FDA, if a company promotes or sells its products on the Web, any accompanying information may be considered "labeling" and subject to FDA labeling requirements.

The FDA permits only agency-approved health claims, namely those backed by "significant scientific agreement." All Web-related content would be subject to regulatory action if the FDA finds the information on the site violates the Federal Food, Drug and Cosmetic Act.

Working Examples

D avid Wright admitted that a lifetime in the commodity dairy business had turned him into a "cynical skeptic."

Separated from the consumers of his milk by the commodity structure he said it was easy to think the worst about human nature. Like many of us, David thought the best thing about farming was that one didn't have to deal with the public.

When his wife, Leianne, told him that she planned to sell her home-made crabapple jelly by placing it on an unattended roadside table in front of the dairy with a coffee can for the money, David was quick to ridicule the idea. Surely the first person who stopped would make off with all of the jelly, the table and the coffee can, he said.

However, when Leianne sold all of her jelly without a single theft of jelly or money but with lots of notes complimenting her for her trust, he said it breached his wall of cynicism and allowed him to think there might be an alternative to the commodity roller-coaster after all.

> *Things are relatively easy to sell if you are willing to take a different marketing approach.*

"Leianne showed me that not only were there a

lot of good people out there but that things were relatively easy to sell if you are willing to take a different
(marketing) approach," he said.

This realization combined with an earlier event
started the gestation of a direct marketing idea. Several
years earlier a real estate developer had approach David
and Leianne about
buying their farm in
Alexandria, Alabama,
for a shopping center
site. They decided not
to sell, but the old real
estate bromide of "location, location, location" being
the source of wealth kept running through his mind.

> *They are always searching for
> other items to add to their "old
> fashioned" marketing niche.*

David and Leianne's Wright's Dairy, fronts on a
very busy non-controlled-access, four-lane highway.
Highway 431 is the main highway between Gadsen and
Anniston in northeast Alabama.

He realized this great location was a total waste
if they stayed in the commodity business and began to
think about direct marketing his farm's milk.

This thinking and investigation stage took up a
year of his rumination time.

David knew that Alabama is a hugely milk-
deficit state. Much of the fluid milk consumed in the
state is hauled in from West Texas. Quality is uniformly
poor and frequently awful.

Also, he liked that fluid milk required minimal
processing equipment and specialized knowledge compared to cheese manufacturing.

For these reasons, he decided to sell his milk as
fluid "sweet milk" (as whole milk is called in the Deep
South) and as "old-fashioned" buttermilk.

He wanted to sell minimum-temperature pasteurized, non-homogenized milk as this would fit both

his personal predilection and the "old-fashioned" image he planned.

As part of his "due diligence" he visited other farms that were attempting to direct market their milk and found their number one problem was supply balance. They either had too many customers for their milk or not enough customers for their milk.

David decided the best way to achieve supply balance right off the bat was to separate the retail end from the production end of the dairy. The production dairy would sell its milk to the co-op as it always had and the retail end would buy the milk from the co-op just like any other dairy processor customer at the standard markup.

> *The number one problem in direct marketing milk is supply balance.*

Of course, this was just a paper transfer but would allow him to start small without worrying about marketing all of the milk he produced. It also allowed him to bypass the Milk Marketing Administration and their paperwork.

To help him with the new processing plant he put a recently retired dairy plant manager on retainer as a consultant. He then started to scour the Internet for information and used dairy processing equipment. By typing in "dairy AND processing" (AND must be in all caps for this to work) on several Internet search engines, he was able to find sites selling used dairy processing equipment. From these sites, Wright was able to assemble all the machinery he needed for his processing plant. Most of this equipment he bought at auction.

For information on dairy processing and plant design, he found the University of Wisconsin dairy site particularly helpful.

The processing plant and retail facility were

combined in an unused 40-year-old milking parlor. A glass wall was put in so customers could watch the milk being processed and bottled. The total cost of the plant and retail facility was around $100,000 of which approximately half was for window-dressing.

The old parlor was painted barn-red, the drive through and parking area was paved and a huge sign advertising the dairy, was erected on the highway.

$1000 A DAY

Wright had hoped for sales of $1000 a day and quickly achieved that level of sales with no advertising other than the roadside sign and publicity in the local newspaper and television. The farm store currently sells "Sweet Milk," Buttermilk, pastured eggs, chocolate chip cookies made from the farm's eggs and butter, and eight different varieties of Amish cheese and "old-fashioned" block type butter.

With an advertising slogan of "Wright Dairy, where the cream still rises to the top," David said the lack of homogenization quickly proved to be a good consumer lure.

"The most common comment we have is about how much creamier the milk tastes."

The combination of low temperature pasteurization (150°F for 30 minutes) produces a milk without the cooked taste high temperature pasteurization produces. David said he personally tastes each batch after pasteurization to make sure it has a flavor as close to raw milk as he can get it.

Customers are offered a free taste before they buy.

The use of whole milk for buttermilk rather than skim also produces a sweeter, less acid product. All customers are offered a free taste of the two milks before they buy.

The Wrights are selling around 300 gallons of milk a day but are producing around 1000 gallons a day from their 150-cow dairy herd. This huge imbalance indicates the wiseness of their supply balancing program and their room to grow. However, David does not plan to grow beyond his current 150 cow herd size.

A drive-up window allows customers to pick up their purchases without getting out of the car.

Wright said that dairies that sell less than 100,000 lbs of milk a month are exempt from much of the worst paperwork and regulation. He said this is around the 150-cow level near where his cow numbers currently are.

300 PERCENT MARKUP ON MILK

Retail milk typically sells for 300 percent more per gallon than farm sale commodity milk. Wright Dairy sells its milk at the same prices as other retail facilities in the area or around $3.00 a gallon. They net one dollar on each gallon after all costs and expected the retail facility to add at least $100,000 to the farm's net income from milk sales in its first year over what selling at commodity prices would have brought. Of course, selling their own milk is only a part of their daily sales.

Eggs are crowd pleasers.

Their own milk and buttermilk only make up around 40% of their daily retail sales. The big surprise was that Amish cheese and butter sales have exceeded fluid milk and buttermilk sales. Wright said apparently the hunger for old fashioned cheese in the South is huge. He said he has a friend that sells $6000 worth of the Amish cheese in a few hours at a local antique flea market each month.

"We actually have a better price markup on the Amish cheese we buy from others than we do on the milk we buy from ourselves," David said.

Another surprise was that "Sweet milk" outsold buttermilk. David thought it would have been the other way around considering the large number of elderly people in the area. However, their consumer group turned out to be younger than he thought it would be with lots of families with young children. "We have attracted every age group with the exception of teenagers," he said.

A drive-through window allows mothers

> *Jim and LeeAnn VanDerPol of Kerkhoven, Minnesota have found that a good way to create new customers for direct meat sales is to cook a dinner for a local small business. The VanDerPols started with their local television station, which not only produced new customers but a lot of good publicity as well.*

with very young children to pick up their purchases without getting out of the car. This has also proven popular with elderly people.

In yet another surprise, the small local Hispanic community turned out to be a big dollar customer. "They love minimally processed, farmstead cheese," David said. "Our average sale per Hispanic customer is around $300."

He said pastured eggs are a major headache to produce but were a sure crowd drawer and were not regulated. He gave his chickens and the egg-mobile to a neighbor, but still sells the eggs through his own farm store. Unfortunately, they sell out of eggs every day by

9:30. A big price increase on the eggs did not slow this sell out time by one second.

"If you are going to have a farm store, you have to have multiple items for sale," David said. "Yes, they come primarily for their milk but people like to shop. They like to have a choice of things to buy." During the summer David and Leianne add jugs of iced tea from a South Carolina tea manufacturer. They are always on the look out for other food items that fit their "old-fashioned" marketing niche. David said the rural South is culturally conservative and he has concentrated on taste and nostalgia.

The Wrights wholesale milk to a local health food store and surprisingly to a quick stop grocery only a short distance down the road from the dairy. This small store sells around $300 a week of the Wright's milk. However, David said he does not plan to pursue additional wholesale outlets.

"I don't want to play the big boys' game of hauling milk to Birmingham and Atlanta. Typically, distribution costs equal processing costs. Because my customer comes to me I have an unfair advantage of at least 50 cents a gallon over the big processors."

David said that direct marketing greatly reduces the minimum size needed to make an excellent income. He had figured that an all-grass, no-grain, organic milk dairy could easily net over $100,000 from just 35 cows

> *Kelly Bruns of Center, Nebraska warns that milk from grassfed cows is very susceptible to off-flavors. He had to quit feeding his cows kelp because his customers complained that the milk had a "fishy" taste.*

producing only 35 pounds of milk a day.

"What we've found is that there is a sizable group of people who do care about the quality of their food. We've found this group of people to be uniformly good people of excellent character. In what other business do your customers thank you for selling to them and offer to overpay? If it hadn't been for Leianne and her crabapple jelly I never would have discovered how many really good people there are out there," David said.

DIRECT MARKETED LEAN BEEF—IN TEXAS

Teddy Roosevelt's orders to his men during the Spanish/American War were to "Do what you can with what you've got where you are." Richard and Peggy Sechrist have taken that advice to heart.

Located on the west side of Texas' "dry line" they realized that a 1000-acre ranch was just too small to provide a living as a traditional ranch. Richard said his father, a successful contractor, regularly lost $100,000 a year on the ranch. Such a level of subsidy was not only philosophically unacceptable, but financially impossible to maintain after his father's death.

In evaluating their problems and opportunities, they decided their biggest opportunity was their ranch's proximity to booming, high-tech-oriented Austin, Texas.

Therefore, they have regeared their ranch from producing commodity priced calves to premium priced, direct marketed, lean beef.

If you try to make one brand fit everyone, it fits no one.

The Sechrists' "Homestead Healthy Foods" brand is marketed direct to consumers in a variety of ways, including the local

Farmers' Market in Fredericksburg, Austin restaurants and health food stores.

They make a net gross margin of $650 a head after all direct costs.

"You can make a good living on a 1000-acre ranch if you direct-market your beef," Richard said. "We figure that 70 animals a year is a living. Anything over that is a real business."

> *A special cooking guide is included with all their beef as lean beef must be cooked slowly to avoid toughness.*

NATURAL BEEF. "Our customer base was created primarily through the recommendation of Naturopath and Homeopath nutritionists in Austin," Peggy said.

While "chemical free" beef has provided them with a natural niche with health conscious and chemically-reactive consumers, it has also kept their beef out of mainstream grocery stores. "The mainstream grocery store sees 'chemical free beef' as a negative claim that could cause the consumer to question the other beef in the store. Therefore, there's no way they are going to take on a niche product that could hurt their primary sales," Peggy Sechrist said. (The meat counter makes up about 40% of the average grocery store's sales and has a considerably higher margin than dry and canned goods.)

LIMITATIONS. While philosophically in agreement with totally organic production, the Sechrists admit it creates production limitations. "We've tried to grow annual ryegrass without nitrogen and all we do is feed the deer," Richard said.

A year around program is also very difficult to achieve without stored forages, particularly in a climate as dry as Fredericksburg. Because of lingering dryness in their area, they have moved their cowherd to East Texas.

TENDER & LEAN. The Sechrists have been using large frame, continental breed cattle. These very slow maturing breeds when killed at 1000 lbs off grass produce an extremely lean carcass. A special cooking guide is included with all their beef as lean beef must be cooked slowly in water or vinegar oil to avoid toughness. The beef is also aged for 7 to 10 days before sale to promote tenderness.

LOW STRESS. Another critical component of tender beef is the way the animal is handled prior to slaughter. Using Bud Williams' low-stress handling techniques, Richard takes the animals to the gate of the kill chute at the packing plant himself. "It is adrenaline in the meat that makes the rib-eye and New York strip cuts tough. I tell the packing plant employees to put their Hot Shots away when they are around our cattle," Richard said.

PROFESSIONAL KILL PLANT. The Sechrists use a USDA inspected kill plant near Austin. This allows their beef to be marketed anywhere in the USA. Also, the professional kill plant knows how to cut beef the way restaurants want it cut, something the smaller state-inspected plants did not know how to do.

The Sechrists cracked the Austin restaurant market by entering some of their beef in a local restaurant chef "cook-off."

ATTENTION CHEFS. The Sechrists cracked the Austin restaurant market by entering some of their beef in a local restaurant chef "cook-off." "The chefs were amazed at how much better our beef tasted,"

Richard said. "Unfortunately, most restaurants only want to buy the tenderloin. We only work with restaurants that will buy all the cuts."

Their hamburger's extreme leanness has produced a major problem in marketing to restaurants. "Our hamburger is about 94% lean and the restaurant trade refuses to take hamburger that is leaner than 80% because it is difficult to cook rapidly without falling apart. If you can't readily market your hamburger, you've got a big problem because hamburger is so much of the carcass yield."

This "too lean" problem has them considering crossbreeding with Angus to give them a fattier hamburger product. However, they worry this could hurt them with their already established health-conscious market. "One of the things you quickly run into with direct marketing is the trade off between the size of a particular niche and the necessity to achieve a certain level of volume to survive economically." Peggy said. "I think that probably what is going to be necessary is to develop several different 'brands' that are specifically targeted to different market niches. If you try to make one brand fit everyone, it fits no one."

Nebraska grazier, Marvin DeBlauw, said retailing grassfed meat is really tough in his very rural area and sometimes he has to sell some animals as feeder cattle. This is not bad in high priced feeder cattle years. In 2001, got $870 a head for his 1000-pound steers as feeder cattle. He would have only gotten $30 more if he had direct-marketed them.

SPREAD THE WORD. Perhaps the biggest niche market they have discovered is the "regional pride" niche. Richard has a slide show about the ranch he presents at local civic clubs. This show does not advocate organic or lean beef but the idea that people should support locally produced farm products. "There are a whole lot of people who just want to support their local farmers and ranchers. They will buy your product just because it is local. They really don't care if it is organic, chemical free, grassfed or whatever," Peggy said.

> *Nebraska grazier, Paul Kleinschmit, has found that people want a smaller ribeye but prefer it to be cut thick—at least three-quarters of an inch. However, they still want it to weight six ounces. This requires a small phenotype animal.*
>
> *He said to be careful to keep your marketing up with your production because this type of animal really takes a hit if you have to sell it through the commodity livestock auction.*

LABELING. Another "label" considering the sizable ethnic tourism business of Fredericksburg could be a German or European style beef product. "Essentially, we are producing European style beef. We might as well have a label for it," Peggy said.

GROUP SALES. Corporate gift boxes have sold well and a local senior citizen program buys 200 lbs of beef a week for its "meals on wheels" program. Copying Tupperware's successful "party marketing," Peggy puts on Homestead Healthy Foods Parties. At these parties attenders see a slide show on the ranch and are given free beef samples. Peggy said these parties usually result in a 100% sale to all attenders.

LISTEN TO YOUR CUSTOMER. "We don't

care if our beef 'fits the box' or not," Richard said. "We let our customers set the standards. As their demands change, we will change." They base their inventory on what their customers have told them they wanted.

SEPARATE BUSINESSES. They feel confident they could market 1000 animals a year if they were available. However, this number of animals is far beyond the production capabilities of their ranch. As a result, they have separated the beef marketing company from the ranch beef production company. It is hoped the beef marketing company can soon market grassfed beef for Texas ranchers located too far from the urban markets to do it themselves.

ADD ONS. In 1998 they added chicken to their meat products. The chickens averaged 4 lbs and sold for $2.50/lb retail, $1.95/lb wholesale. Adding the poultry attracted new customers.

OPEN A STORE. In 1999 they opened Homestead Healthy Food Store at the edge of their small town as an outlet for their organic beef, chicken and eggs. They also sell organic produce grown by other Hill Country farmers.

"We see a gigantic opportunity for regional meat marketing companies," Peggy said. "We hope ours will be successful and can serve as a prototype for others."

50 STEERS A YEAR—IN COLORADO

David and Kay James have been able to turn a small (by Western standards) 550-acre ranch in Durango, Colorado into a living not only for themselves but for four of their five grown children. They have done this by allowing others to "buy into" their pastoral vision by purchasing the ranch's beef, chickens and vegetables.

SHARE YOUR VISION. This "vision" was detailed in a newsletter to their customers. "50 years ago family farms lined the Animas Valley, cultivating the rich soil of the river valley to provide necessary food for the miners in

> *Repeat business is the key to direct market success.*

Silverton and the town of Durango. People knew who grew their potatoes and asparagus and raised their beef; there was a relationship between the family sitting down to eat a meal and the family who grew the meal. We at James Ranch want that back, not only for the health of our family, but for the health of our community. We hope you will join in this vision."

SUCCESS BREEDS SUCCESS. Virginia grazier, Joel Salatin, provided a prototype that they have found workable and to which they have added a few wrinkles of their own. In 2001 they had 150 beef cows, the progeny of which David sells locally as grassfed beef. "We don't put one drop of grain or purchased feed into our cattle. This makes the margins really great when they are sold direct. 50 steers a year produced and sold this way can make an excellent living for a family."

SEASONALITY. The majority of the beef is "harvested" in September and October although the ranch has started over-

> *Egg demand is so great they have to be rationed to customers.*

wintering some steers on winter range to provide an early summer kill as well. These older steers explode on the high quality spring pastures and are ready to slaughter after as little as 30 days of grazing. Steers weigh 900 to 1150 lbs at slaughter.

ON FARM MARKET. The ranch's production

213

is marketed through an on-ranch marketing shed that is open one day a week and through the Durango Farmers' Market on Saturdays. Hamburger, which is the hardest product to sell at a premium price, is sold to local restaurants who tell the ranch's "story" on their

> *Good community public relations are the most cost-effective method of advertising.*

menus. This menu story resulted in the sale of several hundred dollars worth of beef to a tourist from Connecticut while I was there.

The beef is quick frozen after slaughter and double wrapped in white paper for reliable freezer storage. It is sold as pre-cut split halves, halves and as a mostly steak "Premium Grill Package." The halves and splits sell for $2.15 a lb and the Grill Package goes for $197.

REPEAT SALES. Durango has a permanent population of around 15,000. In addition, some 200,000 tourists annually ride the steam-powered, narrow-gauge railroad from Durango to Silverton through the beautiful Animas River Canyon. This railroad runs through the James Ranch. At peak season, eight trains a day puff through the ranch providing great sound effects as they climb the steep mountain grade.

While David loves to hear the trains' daily whistling and chugging, the ranch's marketing efforts are wholly directed to the full-time residents of the town. "The name of the game in direct marketing is repeat business. We largely ignore the tourist trade," he said.

Much more important than tourism to the James' meat sales, Durango is a popular spot for wealthy, early-retirees in their 50s. These people are sophisticated,

well-educated and very discriminating about the food
they eat. It is this group that forms the core of the James
Ranch clientele.

HOLONIC RANCH DEVELOPMENT.
David said he is a strong believer in the division of labor
and self-management. Every member of the family has
their own "holon" or self-managed business that operates within the context of the overall ranch goal.

The cattle are David's "holon."

Kay produces 1200 pastured chickens using
Salatin-style movable pens and a rolling "bear-proof"
hen house produces 70 brown eggs a day. She said egg
demand is so great that they have to be rationed to their
customers and she could easily sell three times her
current number of chickens. The chickens are sold for
$2.50 a pound.

Daughter Jennifer and her husband Joe raise
vegetables and flowers on a "subscription" basis
whereby the customer pays for half of a season's production up front. Their division is known as
Meadowbrook Farm at James Ranch. Jennifer has an
internship program for college students who want to
learn organic production techniques.

Jennifer and Joe are responsible for running the
market stand and the Farmer's Market booth and plan to
add a lodge to the ranch product mix in the near future.

Son Danny and
his wife Rebecca plan to
develop the dairy and
cheese business and
thereby make a full-time
"holon" for themselves.

> *Exhaust all your public rela-
> tions sources first before you
> start advertising.*

"We are looking at producing a non-pasteurized, farmstead cheese. We want a product we can make during
the summer, store and sell year-round," David said.

In a non-food related enterprise, daughter, Julie, and her husband, Johnny, raise landscape trees.

Son, Justin, is in the land reclamation business. This has allowed them to leverage both their grass growing expertise and get part of their cattle wintered at a profit. "People will pay you big bucks to hay your cows on their mine spoils today," David said.

> *California grazier, Joe Morris, said graziers with large minimum purchases (half a beef) and highly seasonal marketing programs like his may find that their customers have not yet consumed all of last year's beef when marketing time comes around again next year. Morris said that they run about a 50 percent repeat business each year.*

"Kay and I want all of our children to live on the ranch, but they understand they will have to create an enterprise that will support them. I read that in England one farm had 1100 different enterprises utilizing different resources of the farm," David said.

On the market day I visited, the on-ranch market stand sold $2200 worth of product. This broke down into $900 worth of chicken, $200 of eggs, $800 of beef, $300 of vegetables and $80 worth of fresh-cut flowers. "Not a bad day," Kay said, "but we've had better ones."

PUBLIC RELATIONS FIRST. David said that good community public relations were the most cost-effective method of advertising. "You need to know your town. Who are the opinion makers? Who are the spheres of influence?"

David said the ranch has given away hamburger

and eggs at the local garden clubs and is a member of the Chamber of Commerce. "Do the easy stuff first. I would exhaust all my public relations avenues before I started advertising." He said they concentrate their public relations efforts in the Christmas party season as that is when people are naturally interacting with each other.

The ranch is open for free customer tours in May each year and only then. Kay said they prized their privacy and did not want to live in a zoo constantly open to outsiders. The ranch has a slide show that they show to local civic clubs and organizations throughout the year.

"Our unfair advantage," David explained. "is that we have a beautiful ranch with highway frontage near a town of sophisticated people. What we have here may not work for everyone, everywhere, but it sure works for us."

LAMB—IN MINNESOTA

Doug Rathke and his wife Connie Karstens own the Liberty Lamb and Livestock Company in Hutchinson, Minnesota.

"At Liberty Lamb our lambs are free to graze," Connie said. "They are also free of hormones and antibiot-

> *Passion alone doesn't pay the bills.*

ics. We're really into freedom including our own."

Doug and Connie direct market between 800 and 1000 grassfed lambs plus grassfed beef and pastured chickens and eggs off 80 grazed acres. Another 50 acres is currently leased to a neighbor for summer crop production but the residues are grazed in the winter.

They began their partnership in 1986 when they married. Doug is a professional sheep shearer and

217

Connie had always had a passion for sheep. However, Connie said that passion alone doesn't pay the bills. They quickly realized that for them to make some real money from a small acreage, they were going to need a wider margin than what commodity lamb offered.

> *Direct marketing all starts with creating a product that is something special.*

"We saw that to increase our profits we had to do two things," She said. "We had to lower our input costs or we had to get a higher price for the product produced. We decided to do both."

She said they first put in a MiG pasture system which tremendously lowered their input costs. This allowed them to graze their sheep for nine months of the year—April through December—and cut their hay feeding to only three months.

For these three months, the sheep eat their way through the hay stack with movable head gates. The British call this technique "horizontal grazing" so I guess you could say that Doug and Connie's sheep graze year-round.

In 1988, Doug and Connie decided they had enough of the commodity business and decided to take control of their prices and lives by direct marketing.

To facilitate year-round direct marketing they decided to use Dorsets, which can lamb year-round. "The Dorset breed suits our needs because they supply a steady year-round supply of fresh lamb for our marketing options," Doug said.

They lamb in February, May and October.

Due to their strict genetic selection, Doug said seedstock sales have become a part of their product mix.

In starting their direct marketing they followed

the recommended route of producing it for themselves, then for their friends and then for their friends' friends.

"There's not a business in the world that doesn't get most of its customers by word of mouth. Direct marketing all starts with your creating a product that is something special."

Doug and Connie admit that starting a direct marketing program is not easy and is very time-consuming but theirs quickly got them off the commodity market roller-coaster. "With a little creativity, some extra hours and consumer savvy, we said good-bye to the middle man and today we direct market everything we raise," Connie said. "And because our markets have expanded so heavily, we also purchase additional sheep from producers within the state that meet our quality standards."

She described the shift to grassfed meats and dairy products as a "tidal wave" that was building out in the ocean. She said direct marketing would be much easier for current graziers than it was for them thanks to Jo Robinson's book *Why Grassfed Is Best*.

They have not sold any sheep through the commodity market for more than 12 years. She said they direct market between 800 and 1000 lambs each year. They also produce and sell

> *Sales to restaurants are notoriously short-lived.*

grassfed Jersey beef, chickens and eggs. Their marketing program consists of a combination of on-farm, restaurant and event sales.

RESTAURANT SALES. Every week they sell six to eight lambs to an ethic restaurant in the Minneapolis/St Paul area. They deliver the lambs in a USDA approved refrigerated trailer. The carcasses are halved down the backbone and cut up by the chef.

"The chef is very particular and has come to rely on us for a top quality supply all year. By dealing direct with our product, they have come to know exactly what we produce," Connie said.

> *Grassfed meat and milk is like a coming tidal wave that's building in the ocean.*

Connie said they planned to expand their restaurant sales in the future but warned newcomers that restaurants are notoriously short-lived. She said she liked ethnic restaurants because they knew how to use the whole carcass, whereas, American restaurants only wanted certain cuts.

STATE FAIR BOOTH. Starting in 1991, Doug and Connie have operated a booth at the Minnesota State Fair. Connie said this 12 day event with 1.5 million attenders produces a large portion of their annual income and is a very intense experience. They have to hire outside employees to work in the booth as the 12 hour days for 12 days are just too tiring for strictly family labor.

"Our most popular item is the lamb gyro. Other items on the menu are lamb burgers, leg of lamb, and lamb wrappers," she said.

The booth gives the farm a lot of good publicity and helps to generate sales throughout the year.

ON-FARM LIVE SALES. Doug said they currently sell about 100 live lambs a year to ethnic communities based on cultural and religious beliefs. He said this business has derived strictly from word of mouth and is hassle-free and requires no licenses.

Another live animal niche is the sale of animals for research purposes. Doug describes the research niche as "demanding but very lucrative."

USDA APPROVED. The centerpiece of their marketing program is an on-farm USDA inspected processing facility. This is in a portion of their home and was the first in-home facility the USDA had ever been asked to approve. The lambs are slaughtered at a nearby USDA plant for $15 a head. Because this facility was so near, Doug and Connie decided to only add a carcass processing facility.

"Our meat is packed by us to insure our precise standards of cutting, trimming and presentation and to be the finest meat in freshness and taste. Excess fat is not tolerated," Connie said.

Connie said an important part of their marketing success was her taking a British Meat and Livestock Commission course in lamb butchering. She also went to a lamb butcher school sponsored by the American Sheep Industry. "We learned where certain glands were and how to remove them to prevent strong off flavors. The average butcher in America has not had enough training to know how to cut up a lamb carcass correctly," she said.

She said that lamb butchering was not particularly difficult to learn and was primarily a game of "practice makes perfect." However, the skills required to cut up a lamb and a steer are entirely different. Since beef butchering skills are more commonly known, they have decided to leave the beef butchering to others and to concentrate on lamb. They cut meat every two weeks. They have to notify the USDA on what

City customers enjoy a country outing and will purchase those products they can't easily find elsewhere.

day they are cutting meat. The inspector is provided free of charge by the USDA.

THE LAMB SHOPPE. In a free-standing small building, they have recently added a retail meat shop called "The Lamb Shoppe." Here they sell lamb, beef, chicken, eggs, woolens and other farm and garden surpluses from time to time. While 75 miles from the Twin Cities, most of their customers come from there and enjoy a "country outing."

She said quality lamb is very difficult to find in America and so serves as their main customer draw. The grassfed Jersey beef is sold for only slightly more than commodity-priced beef and is offered as much as a service to the customer as a profit center. The steers are bought as calves from dairying neighbors and are primarily

The pastured hen eggs are kept in a big wicker basket. The customer is encouraged to pick through the eggs and choose those they want.

used to soak up pasture surplus to the sheep.

Jersey is ranked right behind Angus as one of the most consistently tender meat breeds. They fatten easily on grass and the fat is always a healthy yellow color. Doug said he particularly liked that the Jersey steer could be killed over a wide weight range and still produce a quality product. He said this made it much easier to provide a year-round supply.

"Product diversification is very important to us," Connie said. "Our customers come all this way and want more than one thing for the journey. We always try to keep our minds open to other species that we could layer over our current mix."

Doug and Connie said educating their customers about the health benefits of grassfed meats is an important part of their sales pitch. "While we aren't certified as organic, once they hear our story about the importance of grass-raised animals, they never ask about it again," Connie said.

Direct Marketing Tips for Sheep

In many (most?) areas of the United States, sheep production today also entails the responsibility of developing a local market for your lambs. Almost all those who have bitten the bullet and done it have told me it was far easier than they would have ever believed and would never go back to the "commodity" lamb business. This is particularly true if you are producing a quality, lean lamb.

SMALL IS BEAUTIFUL. If there was ever an animal that lent itself well to direct marketing, an 80 to 100 lb grass finished lamb is it. There are probably far more people willing to commit for a lamb than a whole or half a beef.

CULL EWES & WETHERS. Other producers are trying to band together into slaughter and marketing co-ops. However, the real marketing problem is not the lamb, but the cull ewe and wether. Mutton can make a delicious deep fat fried, fajita-like entree, an excellent Barbecue or a low-fat, easily digestible hamburger. The traditional low price for cull ewes indicates more market neglect than the quality of the meat. There is a real opportunity here for someone with a little meat marketing and promotional flair.

All meat is sold vacuum-packed as frozen cuts. Their biggest retail sales times are weekends, holidays and grilling season.

The lamb sells for $9.95 a pound year-round, year in and year out. Crown rolls are a popular specialty at $14.95 a pound.

She said the price of the lamb is not an objection with their customers who include New York real estate developer, Donald Trump and the rock star known as Prince.

"This is just like going to Grandpa's farm," is a common comment and a sentiment Doug and Connie like to encourage.

"People who come to the Lamb Shoppe leave not only with their purchases, but also with the total experience we have created for them," Connie explained. "We want a very sensory experience for our customers. They see beauty in our pastures and colorful animals, they hear the sounds of lambs baaing, the smell the freshness of nature and feel the wholesomeness of real food raised naturally."

BUFFALO MEAT—IN MISSOURI

Don't call Dan Shepherd's shaggy beasts bisons. They're still called buffalo at Shepherd Farms in Clifford Hill, Missouri, and here's why.

"You don't ask for a `facial tissue' when you need to blow your nose, do you?" Dan asked. "No, you say, `Give me a Kleenex.' You tell the average American you are raising bison and he'll always ask, 'Is that something like a buffalo?'"

Shepherd grazes 240 buffalo cows and their offspring on gamagrass and fescue. The cows calve in May and wean in January. The male offspring are then grown on grass as intact bulls until they are approximately 22 months of age.

The bulls are pasture-slaughtered with a rifle (allowed under Missouri law), bled in the pasture, and the carcass quickly taken to a nearby federally-inspected locker plant for processing. The pasture slaughtering prevents the animals from becoming stressed and producing tough meat.

> *The productive life of a buffalo cow can be as long as 25 years.*

Carcasses average 550 to 650 lbs at an average yield of 60%. The meat is sold frozen and Cryovac packed from an on-farm store to mostly local customers although some is sold nationwide via air freight to buffalo meat enthusiasts.

Buffalos also produce a variety of high priced by-products as well. These include the hide, cape and skull. Dan sells the skulls for $80 a piece for wall decorations. Tanned hides sell for $150 plus $10 per square foot. "People will buy anything from a buffalo," Dan said.

The buffalo cows breed at 3 years of age. Weaning weights range from 350 to 400 lbs and calf gains are slow until the animals become yearlings. "During the summer of their yearling year is when they really turn it on and double their weight," he said. Winter gains tend to be low.

> *If you're a person who might need cash fast, don't consider raising buffalo.*

While slow to get started in life, the productive life of a buffalo cow can be as long as 25 years. Dan said he felt a cow didn't hit her prime until she was 15 to 18 years of age. Calving problems are practically non-existent. Buffalo are extremely heat tolerant and do not need shade.

Because they have not been heavily selected for fertility, buffalo cows tend to "skip" breeding occasionally. Dan said he will allow his cows to skip once, but the second skip turns them into hamburger.

Buffalo are susceptible to the same diseases as cattle including pinkeye, brucellosis and TB and must receive the same vaccinations as cattle. In humid climates like Missouri, they are extremely susceptible to internal parasitism.

Dan described buffalo as "semi-domesticated" animals and describes them as "rambunctious." Fences and working facilities have to be more robust than with cattle. He uses a five-wire, high tensile electric fence for his perimeter fence and two-wire electric fence for interior paddock subdivision. They started using electric fence 13 years ago and in that time they have built 15 miles of electrified fence and only 15 feet of woven wire fence (in a corral wing). "The real money in any ruminant enterprise is selling them for meat. Breeding stock sales come and go but the meat business is steady and constant. I set my prices, not some guys in Chicago." He points out that the price he sets is approximately double what beef sells for. For example, Dan sells sirloin steaks for $7.00 a lb and T-bones for $8.00 a lb. However, production costs are similar if not lower than beef.

Alabama grazier, Charles Ritch, said he noticed a big decline in the response to his direct mail pieces after the terrorist attacks and anthrax mailings in September 2001. He had to supplement his direct mailing with phone calls to old customers to sell all of his 2002 lambs.

"If you are a person who might need cash money

fast, you don't need to get into the buffalo business," Dan explained. "All alternative species are thin markets. This makes it hard to sell large numbers quickly."

He said that like most other things in life the degree of commitment you were willing to make to something determined the amount of success you would ultimately achieve. For example, he experimented with deer production but backed away when he realized he was not willing to make the financial commitment in fencing that adding a commercial scale deer operation would have required.

"I warn everyone who buys a buffalo cow from me that developing a retail meat market is a long hard road, but the money you get from it is real and it will last. The money you will get from seedstock sales can come easier, but it isn't real and it never lasts."

SELLING BUFFALO

WORD OF MOUTH. Almost all of their meat marketing is by word of mouth. Dan said that the nice thing about having a pasture full of buffalo next to the highway is that they will naturally draw a crowd. Dan's wife Jan is in charge of the large on-farm retail store.

HAMBURGER FIRST. Always start a retail program by developing a market for your ground meat because this will be your largest tonnage product. Dan said to concentrate on ground beef marketing and the steaks and roasts will naturally follow. Dan sells his hamburger for $3.25 lb. Roasts go for $4.50 lb, steaks for $7 to $8.50 per pound. Jerky and snack-sticks are good sellers as well.

INCLUE EXTRAS. Recipes and slow cooking instructions are included with each sale.

LIMIT SALES. Never let one customer buy over 20% of your product. It is safer to have a of lot smaller customers than a few big ones. Gift packs "for the person who has everything" are good sellers and are shipped all over the country by next day air in Styrofoam™ shipping containers without dry ice.

GROUP SALES. Sell meat in bulk to family reunions, church and volunteer fire department picnics.

SELL EXTRA INCENTIVES. Other farm products sold through the store are sweet corn and pecans. In the rear of the store is a pecan washing, sorting and cracking operation that provides winter work for two full-time hired hands. The farm currently has 8000 pecan trees.

FREE GIVEAWAYS. Several acres of pumpkins are grown each year and given away to customers. Dan said people will drive 50 miles to get a free pumpkin. "They always feel guilty about getting something for nothing, so they all buy something." He said developing such marketing ideas was crucial to retail success.

For example, he noticed people slowing down and looking at a field full of small white flags that indicated where new pecan trees had been planted. To entice the curious into the store to find out what was going on, they erected a large sign that said "Flag Farm."

THE DOWNSIDE. A downside to retail selling is the requirement to be available for the customer. He said he and his wife Jan were "on-call" 7 days a week with the exception of one week every winter they spend scuba diving in the Caribbean. "The customers will always show up just as you are about to sit down to dinner," Jan said.

Dan agreed but added, "We've found that being willing to do the things no one else is willing to do is where the money is."

Lessons from a Locomotive

In the 1980s, I frequently worked as a weekend relief fireman on a steam-powered tourist railroad on the Mississippi Gulf Coast just east of New Orleans. In subsequent years I have been surprised at how much I learned about firing a coal-burning steam locomotive that applies to marketing. Since firing a steam locomotive is a hard experience to come by these days, I hope you will allow a little digression.

My firing mentor was a grizzled old Louisville and Nashville engineer who didn't take kindly to "college boys," as he described all non-blue collar workers. His "teaching" was usually done at the top of his lungs and with full exasperation. He would frequently shove me aside and take over the firing himself while the engine rolled along with no one at the throttle. Despite his brusque manner, over the years I eventually learned the art of keeping an engine "hot."

You Must Match the Loco to the Load. Steam locomotives working near their maximum load capacity are as fuel efficient as modern diesels. The secret to efficiency was to match the size of the locomotive used to the train hauled. This is why there were many different sized steam locomotives.

The problem with steam locomotives, my mentor explained, was that most of its day was not spent working at maximum load. Much of its day was spent in sidings waiting for other trains, at terminals waiting for passengers to load and unload, or in yards waiting for cars to be added or subtracted from its consist. During all of these non-productive times the locomotive had to be kept "hot" and ready to work when called upon.

> *Businesses have to be built–and financed–slightly ahead of their actual needs.*

A locomotive too big for its task would consume a lot of coal just maintaining its internal heat–or body maintenance, to put this in cowboy terminology. Conversely, a locomotive too small for its load would stall. What was ideal was a locomotive that was just a wee bit more robust than the heaviest load it would be required to haul.

Just like steam locomotives, businesses must be sized to match their markets. Since all new markets necessarily start small, the business and its overhead–body maintenance again–must also be small. However, a business that is too small for its market will stall just like the too-small

> *Since all new markets necessarily start small, the business and its overhead must also be small.*

locomotive. Businesses have to be built–and financed–slightly ahead of their actual needs.

It Takes Time to Build Up a Head of Steam.
When I arrived at work at 5 AM on Saturday morning my locomotive was 46 tons of cold steel full of cold water. The operative word here is cold.

Before I could hope to make any steam, pull any

passengers and make a dollar for the railroad, I had to first heat up all of that cold metal and water. This was a process that required at least two hours, and to a novice fireman the wait seemed interminable.

> *When you first start to market to a "cold" new market it appears that you aren't making much progress for a long time because people are naturally skeptical about new things.*

I had to first build a wood fire and then shovel coal in for an hour and a half before I could even hope to see the steam gauge move one peg off its stop pin. However once the metal and water was hot enough to produce one pound of steam, the remaining steam pressure came up relatively quickly. Old hands expected this delay as normal. New firemen would often not show up early enough to build steam and delay the first train of the day.

In marketing it is the same. When you first start to market to a "cold" new market it appears that you aren't making much progress for a long time because people are naturally skeptical about new things. You have to give yourself the time (and money) it takes to heat a market

> *Once you get it hot never let it get cold again.*

up. Once you get it hot never let it get cold again. If you do, you will have to go through the same expensive and aggravating marketing lag again.

Leave the Station with Everything Perfect and Your Job is Easy. The most critical time in running a steam locomotive was right before you left the station. If you left the station with your steam just below the popping point of the safety valve, your water at the right

231

level in the boiler, and your fire even and new, the run to the next station was easy.

However, if you left the station with too little water in the boiler, too little coal on the fire, or too little steam pressure, your trip was going to be a nightmare because you would be trying to build steam while it was being used. The prospect of this was guaranteed to work a fireman to death. Occasionally, I would just have to stop and let the engine build up steam before continuing.

> *With a new business, make sure you have enough money to last until you get to Breakeven.*

With a business, you need to make sure you have enough money to last you until you get to the first station on the business railroad. This station is called Breakeven. Profit and Return on Total Investment are stations far down the line. These later stations will be reached in time but only if you make it to the first station.

The problem is there is no way to know how much money will be initially required. New markets are not only unknown, they are unknowable. The best rule of thumb is to estimate what you will need and then double that amount.

Make Steam Not Smoke. When I first started firing I thought a rolling continuous pall of smoke from the stack was a great indication of a hard-working, conscientious fireman. However, my mentor told me that creating a lot of smoke was a good way to get fired. In the old steam days making smoke was seen as very wasteful of the company's coal.

"Your job is to make steam, not smoke," he growled at me.

He said that black smoke was an indication that I

was ahead of the fire. In other words, I was putting coal in faster than it could burn. When properly fired, a steam locomotive makes very little smoke. Additional fuel must be kept in balance with its current consumption for maximum steam production.

"You've got to watch your fire and match your firing rate to the consumption," he said.

In direct marketing, it is very easy to get production ahead of sales. Joel Salatin calls this "over-running your headlights." Many farmers and ranchers love to produce and have a tendency to over-produce.

You cannot increase inventory without simultaneously increasing marketing expenditures and effort to increase your customer base. Conversely, if you increase your customer base faster than you can

> *Keeping sales and inventory in balance is absolutely the hardest part of running any business.*

create inventory you run the risk of creating a competitor who will fill your excess demand.

Keeping sales and inventory in balance is absolutely the hardest part of running any business. It is usually learned by doing it incorrectly. In fact, I know of no other way of doing it. The slower you grow the less damaging these imbalances will be.

A Little Coal Often is the Secret. When I first started firing I would load my shovel with all the coal it would hold and heave it into the firebox. This quickly exhausted me. I also noticed that my strenuous efforts not only didn't make much additional steam quickly but actually lowered the steam pressure.

My mentor explained why. He said that fresh coal absorbs heat until it reaches the point where it catches fire. In other words adding fuel to the fire lowers the fire's temperature. In fact, it was actually possible to put the fire out by putting in too much coal too quickly. He said the secret was to put a little bit of coal in, let it catch fire and then put a little bit more in.

> *It is much easier on your cash flow to keep expenses small but regular rather than heavy and infrequent.*

"Don't heap your shovel. Make it easy on yourself and the fire," he said.

This was not only physically a lot easier on me but as he predicted made steam much faster than my previous technique.

Marketing expenditures are the same way. It is much easier on your cash flow to keep expenses small but regular rather than heavy and infrequent. A big part of marketing is giving your message time to sink into your potential customer's consciousness. Those long gaps of total silence are also deadly because whenever potential customers quit hearing from and about you, they assume you have gone out of business. And this belief puts you totally out of their mind's consideration.

Put the Coal Where It Will Burn. In trying to impress my ancient mentor I actually read a 19th century book on how to fire a steam locomotive. I told my mentor that the book said I should fire in a horseshoe pattern with heavy coal in the back corners of the firebox and smaller amounts in each of the far corners.

He looked down his nose at me and just shook his head. "You need to put the coal where the coal will burn."

He opened the firebox door and pointed out the varying colors of the glowing coals. Dark areas indicated where new coal was just trying to get going and where the fire was the coolest. Coal put there would be slow to catch and would not make any more heat. In contrast, the nearly white incandescent areas indicated where the coal was burning hottest and the fastest and was where new coal would catch fire the fastest. He said I should spend less time reading books and more time reading my fire.

In marketing, you also need to learn to read your fire and to feed your successes. None of us wind up

> *Always put your marketing dollars against those items and areas that are selling the best–where the fire is hottest.*

with the business we start out with. Too often we persist in trying to create the business we want rather than the one the customer wants. Most marketing efforts are wasted trying to increase the sales of the slow sellers. This is inefficient. Always put your marketing dollars against those items and areas that are selling the best–where the fire is hottest.

Anticipate the Need for Extra Steam Before You Need It. Because of the time lag between adding coal, getting it burning and making more steam, I had to learn to anticipate any extra upcoming need for extra steam–like a big hill–long before I got there. In other words, my work to get the train over the hill

> *The faster you grow the greater your negative cash flow will become.*

was actually done before the train got to the hill. If I had done everything right, when we got to the hill I got to just sit down and listen to the engine dig in and chug loudly.

In marketing, there is also a time lag between

235

marketing expenditures, sales and collections. This lag is called a negative cash flow and has nothing to do with profitability. Keep in mind that the faster you grow the greater your negative cash flow will become. Therefore, before you put the pedal to the metal make sure you have sources of extra investment or financing lined up first.

Businesses that do not have exterior sources of finance must grow very slowly in order to self-finance their growth.

Knowing the Road is Invaluable. My engineer mentor liked to regale me with tales of his prowess as an engineer. He said his longest work stint was running the daily commuter train from Biloxi to New Orleans. Since this line was located only a few hundred feet inland from the Gulf of Mexico, the morning run in the winter was usually

> *Until you have been over the track a few times, you won't know where the humps and hills are.*

in pea soup fog. He said frequently the only thing he could see was the tiny piece of ground directly beneath his cab window. He had to learn every foot of the roadbed on the eighty-mile run to know where to stop in the dense fog for the many commuter stations on the line.

I was duly impressed and from my short tenure on the tender deck understood what he meant about the importance of "knowing your road."

One of the hardest things to do is to fire an engine over a new line you have never been over before. The first time over you don't know where the hills are and can't build steam in anticipation of them. This makes your work doubly hard because everything new is a surprise.

It's the same way with a new business. Until you have been over the track a few times, you won't know where the humps and hills are. This makes the early days very difficult and stressful.

Unfortunately, the only way it will get better is with time. You cannot know the unknowable and all new businesses are unknowable. You just have to have faith, hang on and initially make it over the road the first time the best way you can.

It will get easier and easier, but there is no way I, or anyone, can keep it from being hard the first time. Just remember that when you are tired, scared, frustrated and mad at how stupid your customers and humans in general are, that what you are feeling is normal. Everyone who has ever started a business of any kind has felt this.

To me riding the train, or even better running the train, was always more fun than any destination. Hopefully, you can make the challenges of building and running a business into something equally pleasurable for yourself.

Go for it!

Author's Bio

Allan Nation has been the editor of *The Stockman Grass Farmer* magazine since 1977. Based in Ridgeland, Mississippi, *The Stockman Grass Farmer* is an international publication that covers management-intensive grassland enterprises. This includes stocker cattle, grass-finished beef and lamb, and pasture-based dairying. Currently it is the only monthly publication in North America devoted solely to management-intensive grassland farming in all its aspects.

The son of a commercial cattle rancher, Nation grew up in Greenville, Mississippi. He has traveled to some 30 countries around the world studying and photographing grassland farming systems. In 1987, he authored a section on management-intensive grazing in the *USDA Yearbook of Agriculture* and has served as a consultant and resource for Audubon Society Television Specials, National Geographic, WTBS, PBS and National Public Radio. He received the 1993 Agricultural Conservation Award from the American Farmland Trust for spearheading the drive behind the grass farming revolution in the USA.

Nation has been a featured speaker at the American Forage and Grasslands Conference (twice), the International Ranching for Profit Conference (twice), the Irish Grasslands Conference, the British Large Herds Conference, the New Zealand Large Herds Conference, the British Grasslands Conference, the Mexican Cattlemen's Association, and the Argentine Agronomy Society. He also delivered the closing remarks at the International Grasslands Conference is Saskatoon, Canada.

He is also the author of *Pa$ture Profits with Stocker Cattle, Grass Farmers, Paddock Shift, Quality Pasture,* and *Knowledge Rich Ranching.*

He lives with his wife, Carolyn, who is also an author, in South Mississippi.

Web Sites

American Agricultural Law Association
    AALA
    University of Arkansas, College of Law
    Fayetteville, AR 72701
    www.aglaw-assn.org

ATTRA—Appropriate Technology Transfer for Rural Areas
    ATTRA
    University of Arkansas
    PO box 3657
    Fayetteville, AR 72702
    800/346-9140
    www.attra.org

Dr. Tilak Dhiman, Assistant Professor, Utah State University–
CLA research and meat testing
    Department of Animal, Dairy and Veterinary Sciences
    College of Agriculture
    Logan, UT 84322-4815
    435/797-2155
    trdhiman@cc.usu.edu

Farmer/Consumer Links
    www.localfarm.net

Farmer Direct Marketing, USDA
www.ams.usda.gov/directmarketing

Farmers' Markets
Agricultural Marketing Service Farmers Market
Directory
www.ams.usda.gov/farmersmarkets/map.htm

The Food Alliance
To promote marketing of food raised by farmers using
sustainable practices.
The Food Alliance
1829 NE Alberta, Suite 5
Portland, OR 97211
503/493-1066
FAX: 503/493-1069
www.thefoodalliance.org

Food & Drug Administration (FDA)
Food labeling regulations and guides.
FDA, Center for Food Safety
200 C Street, SW
Washington, D.C. 20204
www.fda.gov

Great Plains Buffalo Association
Bison producers who believe grassfed is best.
Great Plains Buffalo Association
PO Box 243
Seward, Nebraska 68434
www.gpbuffalo.org.

Internet Marketing Center
Tips, strategies, research resources, monthly newsletter
www.marketingtips.com

Jo Robinson

A good place to check out the competition in your area. Includes the locations of hundreds of grassfed meat and milk producers in the United States. The news section is your best place to keep up with all the latest health news and documented research about the benefits of grassfed meat and dairy products.
www.eatwild.com

Mazes by Brett Herbst

www.cornfieldmaze.com

Minnesota Institute for Sustainable Agriculture

Links to other states.
The Minnesota Institute for Sustainable Agriculture
411 Borlaug Hall
1991 Beuford Circle
St. Paul, MN 55108
800/909-6472
www.misa.umn.edu

National Organic Program

http://www.ams.usda.gov/nop

North American Farmers' Direct Marketing Association (NAFDMA)

62 White Loaf Road
Southampton, MA 01073
888/884-9270
www.nafdma.com

State Regulations

List of state departments of agriculture.
www.ink.org/public/kda/stateags.html

Sustainable Farming Connection
Farmers forum, resources, marketing links
http://metalab.unc.edu/farming-connection

Bibliography

Dohner, Janet Vorwald. *The Encyclopedia of Historic and Endangered Livestock and Poultry Breeds.* New Haven, Connecticut: Yale University Press, 2001.

Dunaway, Vicki. *The Small Dairy Resource Book.* Beltsville, Maryland: Sustainable Agriculture Network, January 2000.

Gladwell, Malcolm. *The Tipping Point, How Little Things Can Make a Big Difference.* Boston, Massachusetts: Little, Brown and Company. 2000.

Godin, Seth. *The Big Red Fez, How to Make Any Web Site Better.* New York: Fireside Book, Simon & Schuster, 2001.

Hamilton, Neil D. *The Legal Guide for Direct Farm Marketing.* Des Moines, Iowa: Drake University, 1999.

Kantor, Sylvia. "Internet Marketing for Farmers." Agriculture and Natural Resources Fact Sheet #510. King County Cooperative Extension, Washington State University, 1998.

Lee, Andrew W. *Backyard Market Gardening, The Entrepreneur's Guide to Selling What You Grow.* Columbus, North Carolina: Good Earth Publications, 1996.

Macher, Ron. *Making Your Small Farm Profitable.* Pownal, Vermont: Storey Books, 1999.

"Marketing Strategies for Farmers and Ranchers." Sustainable Agriculture Network. www.sare.org/san/htdocs/pubs/

Moyer, Brian. "This is not your father's farm." *Passages.* Fall, 2001.

Index

V

W

Y

Z

More from Green Park Press

FARM FRESH, Direct Marketing Meats & Milk by Allan Nation. 101 working examples of North American grass farmers who are direct marketing grassfed products. An excellent companion to **Grassfed to Finish.** Softcover, 256 pages. **$30.00***

GRASSFED TO FINISH, A production guide to Gourmet Grass-finished Beef by Allan Nation. A gourmet grassfed product is not only possible year around, but can be produced virtually everywhere in North America. This book shows how to create a forage chain of grasses and legumes to keep things green and growing every month of the year. Softcover. 304 pages. **$33.00***

KNOWLEDGE RICH RANCHING by Allan Nation. In today's market, knowledge separates the rich from the rest. **Knowledge Rich Ranching** details how to read and profit from the cattle cycle. It reveals the secrets of high profit grass farms and ranches, and explains family and business structures for today's future generations. Anyone who has profit as their goal will benefit from this book, the first to cover the business management principles of grass farming and ranching. Softcover, 336 pages. **$32.00***

NO RISK RANCHING, Custom Grazing on Leased Land by Greg Judy. Based on his first-hand experience, Greg Judy shows how to make a living from the land without owning it. By custom grazing on leased land he was able to pay his entire farm and home loan within three years. Today he has ten farms, including his own totaling 1560 acres, and grazes more than 1200 stockers, cow-calf, and replacement heifers. **No Risk Ranching** tells how to find idle land to lease, calculate the cost of the lease, develop good water on leased land, figure fencing costs, lower risk through custom grazing and includes contract examples. Softcover, 240 pages. **$28.00***

More from Green Park Press

MANAGEMENT-INTENSIVE GRAZING, The Grassroots of Grass Farming by Jim Gerrish. Covers the basics of MiG grazing such as why pastures should be divided into paddocks, how to tap into the power of stock density, extending the grazing season with annual forages and much more. Chapter summaries include action tips for putting each lesson to work. Softcover, 320 pages. **$31.00***

PA$TURE PROFIT$ WITH STOCKER CATTLE by Allan Nation. Nation illustrates his economic theories on stocker cattle by profiling grazier, Gordon Hazard. Hazard accumulated and stocked a 3000-acre grass farm solely from retained stocker profits and without bank leverage. Nation backs his theories with dollars and sense budgets, including one showing investors how to double their money in a year by investing in stocker cattle. Softcover, 192 pages **$24.95***

QUALITY PASTURE, How to Create It, Manage It, and Profit from It by Allan Nation. No nonsense tips for boosting profits with livestock. Shows how to build quality pasture from the soil up. Details how to match pasture quality to livestock class and stocking rates for seasonal dairying, beef production, baby calf rearing, and multi-species grazing. Includes working examples of real people making real profits. Softcover, 288 pages. **$32.50***

SHELTER & SHADE, Creating a Healthy and Profitable Environment for Your Livestock with Trees by John & Bunny Mortimer. Shows how to use trees and landscape for shelterbelts, fodder, and beneficial habitats for stock. By working with Nature trees can eliminate the need for costly confinement structures, lower the need for purchased feeds, and add to your bottom line as well as the beauty of your farm. Covers planting design, plus trees to use for shelter, shade, birds, bees and browse. Softcover, 151 pages. **$20.00***

To order call 1-800-748-9808
or visit www.stockmangrassfarmer.com

* plus shipping & handling

Questions
about grazing ??????
Answers *Free!*

Green Park Press books and the *Stockman Grass Farmer* magazine are devoted solely to the art and science of turning pastureland into profits through the use of animals as nature's harvesters. To order a free sample copy of the magazine or to purchase other **Green Park Press** titles:

Please make checks payable to
Stockman Grass Farmer
PO Box 2300
Ridgeland, MS 39158-2300

1-800-748-9808
or 601-853-1861
FAX 601-853-8087

Shipping:	Amount	Canada	Mexico
Under 2 lbs	$4.95	$7.50	$7.50
2-3 lbs	$6.25	$8.50	$12.00
3-4 lbs	$7.00	$10.00	$15.00
4-5 lbs	$8.50		
5-6 lbs	$10.25	We ship 4 lbs per package	
6-8 lbs	$13.50	maximum outside USA.	
8-10 lbs	$16.50	Foreign Postage: Add 40% of order.	

Name _____

Address _____

City _____

State/Province _____ Zip/Postal Code _____

Quantity	Title	Price Each	Sub Total
____	**Farm Fresh** (weight 1 1/2 lb)	$30.00	_____
____	**Grassfed to Finish** (weight 1 1/2 lb)	$33.00	_____
____	**Knowledge Rich Ranching** (weight 1 1/2 lb)	$32.00	_____
____	**No Risk Ranching** (weight 1 1/2 lb)	$28.00	_____
____	**Management-intensive Grazing** (weight 1 1/2 lb)	$31.00	_____
____	**Pa$ture Profit$ with Stocker Cattle** (1 lb)	$24.95	_____
____	**Quality Pasture** (weight 1 1/2 lb)	$32.50	_____
____	**Shelter & Shade** (weight 1 lb)	$20.00	_____
____	Free Sample copy *Stockman Grass Farmer* magazine		

Sub Total _____

Postage & handling _____

Mississippi Residents add 7% Sales Tax _____

U.S. Funds Only, Please   TOTAL _____

Name _____

Address _____

City _____

State/Province _____ Zip/Postal Code_____

Quantity	Title	Price Each	Sub Total
____	**Farm Fresh** (weight 1 1/2 lb)	$30.00	_____
____	**Grassfed to Finish** (weight 1 1/2 lb)	$33.00	_____
____	**Knowledge Rich Ranching** (weight 1 1/2 lb)	$32.00	_____
____	**No Risk Ranching** (weight 1 1/2 lb)	$28.00	_____
____	**Management-intensive Grazing** (weight 1 1/2lb)	$31.00	_____
____	**Pa$ture Profit$ with Stocker Cattle** (1 lb)	$24.95	_____
____	**Quality Pasture** (weight 1 1/2lb)	$32.50	_____
____	**Shelter & Shade** (weight 1 lb)	$20.00	_____
____	Free Sample copy *Stockman Grass Farmer* magazine		

Sub Total _____

Postage & handling _____

Mississippi Residents add 7% Sales Tax_____

U.S. Funds Only, Please   TOTAL _____

■■■■■■■■■■■■■■■■■■■■■■■■■■■■■■■■■■■■■■

Shipping:	Amount	Canada	Mexico
Under 2 lbs	$4.95	$7.50	$7.50
2-3 lbs	$6.25	$8.50	$12.00
3-4 lbs	$7.00	$10.00	$15.00
4-5 lbs	$8.50		
5-6 lbs	$10.25	We ship 4 lbs per package	
6-8 lbs	$13.50	maximum outside USA.	
8-10 lbs	$16.50	Foreign Postage: Add 40% of order.	

Please make checks payable to
Stockman Grass Farmer
PO Box 2300
Ridgeland, MS 39158-2300

1-800-748-9808
or 601-853-1861
FAX 601-853-8087

Green Park Press books and the *Stockman Grass Farmer* magazine are
devoted solely to the art and science of turning pastureland into profits
through the use of animals as nature's harvesters. To order a free sample
copy of the magazine or to purchase other Green Park Press titles: